Indiana

Franklin H. May
1949

PREHISTORIC MAN:
THE GREAT ADVENTURER

Stormbound

PREHISTORIC MAN:

THE GREAT ADVENTURER

by

CHARLES R. KNIGHT

APPLETON-CENTURY-CROFTS, INC.
New York

W

PRINTED IN THE UNITED STATES OF AMERICA

This book is affectionately dedicated to three descendants of Prehistoric Man— my wife, my daughter and her husband.

C.R.K.

IN APPRECIATION

During my years of study of the difficult subject of Prehistoric Life in general, there have been naturally certain men with whom I have conferred and also discussed the probable forms, habits and environment of many types of extinct creatures. Man himself, because of his unique and tremendously interesting personality has occupied a prominent place in these careful surveys of the conditions that once existed upon our planet. I therefore take pleasure in expressing my appreciation to those who have given me unstintingly and generously of their own special ideas upon the subject. I remember for example with what almost boyish enthusiasm the late Prof. Henry F. Osborn and myself went into the matter of the probable facial contours and body proportions of both the Neanderthal and Cro-Magnon of western Europe as well as their implements, environment and cultures. Prof. Osborn was not merely a student of the life of the past, but a lover of modern animals as well, so that even in those early years of our acquaintance we realized the necessity for a comparison of both modern and fossil types in our reconstruction of any extinct form. This method of approach, almost unique in its day, has long since been recognized as the surest and most logical routine by which a satisfactory result can be obtained in this very difficult field. There are many other friends in the scientific world to whom I would like to refer, among them Dr. K. C. Nelson of the American Museum of Natural History, Dr. J. H. McGregor of Columbia University, already mentioned in the text, and Dr. William K. Gregory, American Museum anatomist, an expert on the structure of vertebrates in general. Dr. Ekholm, a specialist in the Maya culture of Yucatan (also from the American Museum) and the late William D. Matthew, Professor of Paleontology from the same great institution. In Washington the late Dr. A. Hrdlicka, valiant champion of the not too great antiquity of man in America, and Dr. Dale Stuart, American anthropologist at the National Museum. In Europe, the Abbé Henri Breuil, with whom our cave trip was made. Prof. Marcellin Boule of the Museum of Paleontology in Paris, and Sir Arthur Keith and Sir Grafton Elliot-Smith in London. To the late Dr. Franz Weidenreich I owe special thanks for his untiring efforts to bring to my attention certain outstanding characteristics of some of the more primitive forms of early man, discovered in China and Java. Chief among these were his ideas on the form and size of a hypothetical

Chinese man of vast proportions—*Gigantopithecus*, known only from three huge molar teeth discovered by Dr. von Koenigswald in a drugstore display in Hong Kong, China. The Peking man (*Sinanthropus*) and certain skulls and jaws of the *Pithecanthropus* races also came in for long discussions, and these talks were most valuable to me, as the specimens were fragmentary and required the scrutiny of experts to determine their full value. To all these friends and many others, again my sincere thanks and appreciation for all their time, trouble and the inspiration for the carrying out of what has been to me a lifelong pleasure.

CHARLES R. KNIGHT

CONTENTS

CONTENTS

LIST OF ILLUSTRATIONS

xiii

PREHISTORIC MAN:
THE GREAT ADVENTURER

MAN AND THE ELEMENTS

To most of us, the glacial periods in world history, eras about which we have read in our geologies, seem of very little importance, so far removed are they from the present-day conditions of existence. Neither can we grasp the idea of the profound changes of climate upon animal and vegetable life entailed by a constant lowering of the average yearly temperatures in any given region. But the records show that during a period of several hundred thousand years, the continent of Europe was subjected to at least four periods of ice and glacial action interspersed with ages of somewhat warmer climates. Earlier man's initial appearance in this region had taken place before the first great ice advance, but it was not until the close of the third interglacial stage that the Neanderthal people arrived from some far eastern land. Fortunately they were a tough and hardy race of primitive savages, because terrible years lay ahead—years when deep snows, steadily dropping temperatures, and fierce winter gales bit deeply into the vitality of these unfortunate adventurers. Yet they bravely and tenaciously clung to their dreary cave habitations high on steep and rocky cliffs, building great fires, killing game with spears, clubs and stone hand axes. There, feasts were prepared, the flesh of slain animals greedily devoured, and the warm furry hides later roughly sewed together to make crude garments for protection against severe weather. Thus fortified, they dared nature to do her worst, sustained as they were in adversity by the unconquerable spirit of man.

Here we see a family of these lowly but undaunted folk upon their way across a low pass to better hunting fields. Trapped upon a bleak and exposed promontory, they patiently await the passing of a terrific gale of wind and sleet as it sweeps down from the higher reaches of the great snow peak towering menacingly above them. The long white plume of snow particles driven sideways by the fierce gusts glows like a warning pennant against the dark sky, while the first spears of the coming storm beat relentlessly upon the little huddled group of shivering humanity. Perhaps a shade of fear enters the hearts of these primitive beings as they gaze upward and elements rage about them, blotting out the glacier in the valley below. Frustrated for the time being, they still display in their attitudes that courage, doggedness, strength, and indifference to privation so evident in the lives of our ancestors. Had it not been so, humanity would long ago have vanished into oblivion.

MAN IN AN ANIMAL WORLD

Even today, in this the twentieth century of our era, the element of time and the profound changes which the passing of the ages have exerted upon our planet are still only vaguely realized by a majority of civilized people. Yet the truth is that everything both animate and inanimate does change in one way or another as the centuries roll away. Mountains rise only to be worn down at last to their very foundations, continents are altered in their size and form, and oceans flow over what was once dry land, or are thrown back again into the depths by some titanic upheaval of the Earth's crust.

For countless eons of basic adjustment, there was no living thing to be found either upon the lands or in the waters which surrounded them. The factor of time, however, was gradually to reverse this all-pervading sterile condition of a primordial Earth—time, and the advent of that mysterious force which motivates us all. Thousands of millions of years have come and gone since those first evidences of sentient being. During that majestic interval the germ of life has never ceased to function, although the forms which are the offspring of that life have altered again and again. The wondrous procession of plants and animals spread widely across the tremendous periods

of geologic time shows clearly, now that we partially understand the facts, a progressive evolution
from the more primitive forms to those with higher
levels of intelligence and physical adaptation. On
that vast chart of nature's handiwork, the fifty million years of the Age of Mammals seem small indeed,
and the period of man's emergence from a purely
animal existence into that of a creature with extreme
potentialities for mental advancement occupies only
a meager space at the top of that stupendous record.

But within that space there are those of us who
believe they can distinguish indications of a magical
something which has entered into the primitive structure of man's personality—a new attribute tran-
scending time and even life itself. Fortified by the
extraordinary virility of this inspiration, man has
acquired, among a host of other things, certain priceless gifts: the ability to project his thoughts beyond
all mundane bounds, even into the sublime regions
of the spirit, to understand the difference between
good and evil, and to have visions of a Supreme
Being and of a life beyond the grave. Thus, mammal
though he be, he stands unique, endowed by grace,
as has no other creature since the beginning of life
itself.

In direct contrast to the conception of his spiritual
origin and subsequent paternal guidance, man has

gradually come to be regarded by many scientists as a culminating type of mammal—a product of certain characteristics of body and mind, which eventually through long ages merged into a two-legged, upright-walking creature of exceptional mental ability. We still do not know the complete story of his ancestry, nor are we able to predict with any assurance his ultimate destiny. Reams have been written about him, for after all he is by far the most intensely interesting animal that ever trod this earth. Nevertheless, it seems strange that he of the thousands of animated beings of which we have knowledge should have so immeasurably surpassed them all in mental accomplishment. Serious thinkers in many lands bear witness to the paramount difficulty of explaining this highly engrossing phenomenon.

It would seem that various religious faiths long ago settled to their own satisfaction the question of man's ancestry by ascribing his advent to the beneficence of a Divine Creator. On the other hand, certain individuals of the scientific community are prone to regard him merely as evidence of chemical reaction carried to a high degree of perfection. By and large, however, the great mass of the people have always, even in classical times, entertained more or less confused opinions on the entire subject, leaning one way or the other according to their natural proclivities, or allowing themselves to be guided by certain trends of religious or secular thought.

Today we are standing at the crossroads of man's material destiny, not knowing just which way to turn. Nor can we escape from our difficulties through the fog of uncertainty which surrounds them. Confronted by dangers and problems largely of our own making, it behooves mankind to closely watch each step along the dark and dangerous way. However, we are not here concerned with the present status of the human race from either an ethical or a political standpoint, but the long history of our early ancestors does certainly intrigue our imagination to a remarkable degree.

Curiously enough the extreme complexity of man's personality has proved a barrier rather than a help to any investigation of his true status in a world of animal life. To the mystical mind he appeared a sanctified being quite apart from all other living things, by virtue of his supposedly godlike attributes, and as such did not need to be investigated or classified in any other way. So profoundly was this idea a part of ancient and indeed quite recent historical thought that even men whose opinions followed strictly realistic lines were more or less influenced in their search for the truth by the mass of theories and positive convictions which had accumulated dur-

ing the centuries before and after the beginning of
the Christian era.

This reaction to objective research was not easily
dispelled, though from time to time as the ages
passed certain able and advanced thinkers in many
countries had succeeded in glimpsing in a more or
less vague way the long-hidden paths that led far
back into a dim and barely suspected realm of ancient
life. It is surprising, nevertheless, to realize that until
somewhere along the middle of the last century between 1830 and 1860 little definite work on man's
true relationships and scientific classification in the
scheme of nature had been accomplished, and his
ancestral line had not been clearly indicated. The
world apparently was not yet ready to assimilate
any profound observations relative to our early history, but the time was not far off when certain major
discoveries of the remains of ancient man were at
last to concentrate scientific research upon the problems which these discoveries suggested.

In the year 1848, Lieutenant Flint, an Englishman,
had discovered on the Rock of Gibraltar a fairly
well-preserved skull of an early type of human being. Little guessing the future importance of this
find, he sent the skull to England, where it finally
became the property of the Royal College of Sur-
geons in London. At that time, however, even this
momentous event was barely appreciated by savants

who might have been supposed to know better, and its tremendous import did not become apparent until some years later.

Fate seemed determined to center attention upon the value of this line of research so that when, in 1856, a second skull resembling the first specimen was unearthed near Dusseldorf in Germany, its discovery caused widespread controversy and speculation. The particular site of the find, the Neander Valley, furnished a suggestion for the scientific name of the creature, *Homo Neanderthalensis,* or Man of the Neander Valley. In addition to the skull other bones, which perhaps belonged to the same individual, completed the most valuable evidence of ancestral humanity discovered up to that time.

Reactions to the true significance of this remarkable fossil differed greatly, according to the individual point of view held by various eminent specialists taking part in the controversy. Thus for some extraordinary reason the great evolutionist, Charles Darwin, was not greatly impressed by a specimen which was really a supreme confirmation of his theories on that most important subject. But his intimate friend and fellow worker, Thomas Huxley, himself a superb anatomist, was deeply intrigued. After a close study of the remains he saw in them a new and primitive type of human being of excessively ancient lineage. Schaffhausen, a German expert, also recognized in the specimen distinctly primitive traits lower than our own species in every particular, and he constantly held to this opinion in spite of the opposition expressed by some of his colleagues. On the other hand Virchow, a most distinguished man of learning, was positive that the skull was that of an idiot or a deformed type of modern man. Thus the rather acrimonious battle of opinions raged for some time between these profound scholars—although the final outcome was favorable to those who had held out for the recognition of an early species of man with characteristics which removed him from the recent examples known as *Homo sapiens.*

It is safe to say that the discovery of these bones and the intense interest which the event created might easily be held responsible for the birth of a new and special brand of science, which we call prehistory, or the study of man before the beginning of the written word. Nevertheless, the advocates of the new science were to run into bitter opposition from certain individuals with strong religious convictions. But the advance of scientific knowledge, fortified by an ever-increasing tide of actual evidence in the shape of bones, skulls, implements, and weapons soon contributed to the settled opinion that at last science was on the right track. Subsequent discoveries were eventually to carry man's history back to an antiquity undreamed of by earlier students of the subject. Added to these encouraging circumstances, an aroused and tremendously interested public gave full rein to their innate curiosity about such matters, and the rehabilitated study of man's ancestry was launched upon an ever-widening sea of controversy and speculation.

As we now realize, the date of these epoch-making events coincided more or less closely with Darwin's revolutionary statements on the descent and the evolution of man from a line of vastly lowlier creatures whose ancestry extended back into a very remote past—to a period in fact when the Age of Mammals was in its infancy after having emerged from a long Reptilian Era dominated by huge dinosaurs on the land and equally terrifying marine monsters of many species and types. We do not know the reasons, except to a limited extent, which led to the extinction of these huge cold-blooded creatures, but it may be that some drastic changes in living conditions contributed largely to their final disappearance.

Naturally a still more remote stage lay behind the Reptilian Era (more specifically the Triassic, Jurassic and Cretaceous ages), an immense time period of several hundred million years duration. Even lowlier creatures, primitive lizardlike animals, and before them in the coal-making or Carboniferous

time, salamanders and other newtlike species
crawled about on the land or swam in the warm,
sluggish streams and lakes of that far-off day. Be-
sides all these, a great array of fishes and invertebrate forms, including insects, have all left evidences
in the shape of fossilized remains of their former
existence. These souvenirs of an earlier time lie
scattered through the soil and in the rocks of every
country in the world. The stony relics have intrigued
scholars for generations.

Egyptians, Greeks, Romans and, in later centuries,
the best minds in Europe have puzzled over the recurrent deposits of shells, leaves, and bones of animals whose appearance in unusual places made it
certain that they had been buried for a very long
time. The profound reasoning power displayed by
many ancient investigators resulted in some very
able and astute conclusions regarding the origin
of these interesting relics. As a rule, however, the
data was fragmentary and the available literature
practically nonexistent, while the public reaction was
generally that of the curio collector or the super-
stitious ignoramus who regarded all such objects
either with dread or repugnance. Yet the subject
really was one of great complexity, and in spite of a
vast amount of deep thinking, research, and speculation the true significance of the advent of life upon
this earth, as well as its continued existence, pro-

gression, and immensely diversified expression, was
not thoroughly appreciated during the earlier periods
of civilized history.

Sporadic theories and conjectures had appeared at
intervals, but it was not until a hundred years or so
before the apparently crucial period of the Nineteenth Century, when the study of man as an animal
became a subject of such prime importance, that
various experts in the natural sciences began to
assemble their respective talents in an effort to better
understand the world in which they existed. This
coterie of brilliant scholars, working along many
lines of research, delved deeply into the causes, relationships, and evident results of the intermingling
of natural forces as expressed in the animal and plant
life of our planet. It is reasonable to suppose that
Darwin and his able contemporaries were profoundly
influenced by the force and logic of deductions in
widely diversified scientific fields. Geology, botany,
zoology, glaciers and their effect on climate and animal life—these and a host of other interlocking and
pertinent subjects could but serve to crystallize and
elucidate the enormous problems of evolution then
coming to the forefront of scientific thought and
speculation.

Man and his place in a world of animal life was to
fill a large space in these investigations, and the discovery of the Neanderthal Man remains and their

actual place in our history presented a concrete challenge for further exploration in a virtually unknown but exceedingly important field. It became apparent that this extraordinary being must have been descended from ancestors still lower in the human scale, and these in turn receded even more deeply into the mists of antiquity, always departing further and further from the manlike type.

Once it became necessary to recognize him as an animal, man had to be traced back, if possible, to some very remote stage of creation—a stage wherein he might not have resembled a man at all either in size or general appearance. In any case, man's ancestor had to be a creature whose physical characteristics bore a distinct similarity in its profound anatomical construction to our own peculiar type of body and brain formation. This line of research was evidently one for the expert anatomist skilled in the science of deduction, comparison, and recognition of all the salient points of difference and resemblance between various species of animals as evidenced in their skeletal framework and dentition.

To Darwin and many of his confreres, the little animal known to us as a lemur seemed to best fulfill these requirements, although to the layman the selection may not appear especially appropriate. We can rest assured, however, the choice was a correct one, because even today this goggle-eyed, long-tailed, tree-living animal is regarded as our logical long-ago ancestor. To those of us who visit zoological gardens, the lemur species most frequently exhibited is the so-called ring-tailed variety; an animal about the size of a cat, whose caudal appendage is normally carried in a gracefully S-shaped curve high above the back. As a family, these funny wide-eyed agile animals come mainly from Madagascar, the large French-owned island off the east coast of Africa. They are nocturnal and live on fruits and possibly animal food such as insects, birds' eggs, and even the young birds when they can catch them.

Lemurs are extremely active animals though nocturnal in habits when they come out at night on their trips in search for food. Nevertheless, should a lemur be awake when an onlooker arrives in a zoo, the fortunate individual will be treated to an exhibition of astounding jumps, somersaults, hand-springs, and barwork rarely performed by any other creature. Otherwise, they seem to the untrained eye singularly stupid and unprepossessing animals, staring about with their direct front gaze set in an expression of hopeless imbecility. One must admit that as an ancestor the lemur does not quite come up to our ideas on such a serious matter. Alas, the thought merely demonstrates one's ignorance of those deeper anatomical resemblances between the lemur and ourselves. After all, why should this futile-appearing stranger have been honored by our relationship to him and his very early progenitors? Why should the great Darwin and many other zoologists have selected him from a host of other mammalian types?

The answer to this question is really quite simple when we realize that the lemur in his general and even his specific anatomy exhibits a series of characteristics which foreshadow those of the great apes, and consequently of man himself. In reaching this conclusion, the expert anatomist studies with great care the shape, arrangement, and number of the teeth in man and the ancestral type. He also scrutinizes with deliberation the conformation and bulk of the brain cavity in the fossil lemurs, the recent species, and our own top-heavy effort in that direction. From such beginning he examines minutely every other part of the skeleton, especially the bones of the hands and feet because resemblances and differences at these crucial points tell us much that we would like to know about the peculiarities of our foot and hand structures. Nothing is left to chance in his searching comparisons and our lemurlike relatives are investigated down to the last bone in their little bodies. The muscular and nervous systems in the living species undergo the same intensive methods of dissection and analysis as are lavished upon our own complex mechanisms. Although he fulfills undoubted qualifications as a precursor of our human stock, the lemur does not apparently appeal to every scientific school of thought. There are some dissenters who prefer the tarsier as the creature much better fitted for the position. This ferocious big-eyed midget is even more unattractive in general appearance than our lemuroid relative, but his advocates are vociferous in their assertions that he is the right fellow for the place.

This discussion, which bids fair to shake the very foundations of our long-ago conceived ideas as to who is who in the primate family, must be left in other hands than ours. It is enough for us to know that the most expert minds among our particular brand of scientists still consider the lemur as quite able to fulfill all the requirements of a very distant relative of our own race, and as such he would occupy a position far down among the lower branches of our family tree—a tree which has been growing for perhaps forty million years.

There is still another disagreeable little beast that has been nominated by certain specialists as a possible contender for genealogical honors—a peculiar type of mammal known as the tree shrew. The creature has a long snout, a short rather pointed tail carried in an upcurve, a rounded back, and a most unpleasant way of moving in a series of quick jerks from place to place. It is generally fierce, aggressive, and not

Gigantopithecus and saber-toothed tiger in mortal combat

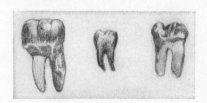

Comparative study of molar teeth (reduced ⅓) (Left to right)
Gigantopithecus, man, gorilla

The Gigantopithecus

at all intelligent. In fact, none of the three animals cited as being our possible distant relative gives the impression of having a superior mentality.

All these early progenitors, if indeed they are such, really make little difference to us as modern human beings simply because they are so very ancestral and, it must be confessed, a rather scrubby, stupid, and altogether uninteresting lot so far as general appearance goes. Unfortunately we cannot quite get away from the disturbing thought that somewhere at some time we have all seen people who reminded us in one way or another of a member of this ugly trio. The fellow on the ocean trip who emerged from the smoking room in a whisky-and-soda daze stared about him just as foolishly and helplessly as our cousin, the lemur. Or we remember the type of somewhat sinister and ferocious human with large bright unseeing eyes who was not really blind, but suspicious and frightened—too much tarsier perhaps in his cosmos!

Of course, when it comes to the great apes, we don't even have to stretch a point. They are in very truth related, painfully like us, and ridiculously excellent though not exact duplicates of ourselves in many diverting ways. These we don't mind especially, but the lemur, tarsier, and tree-shrew crowd seem to us, in spite of the scientists, a most depressing set of forbears. However what really interests us in

this connection are the approximate dates and loca-
tion of man's first appearance as a human animal.

Was it perhaps three hundred thousand, a million, a million and a half years ago, and where? No
scientist seems willing to be quoted definitely on this
question. The Neanderthal Man of Europe was at
any rate supposed to have lived some forty thousand
years ago, but his earlier relatives, *Pithecanthropus*
from Java, might have wandered about in the jungle
for three hundred thousand years down the line of
prehistory. No one can be at all certain about these
figures: they must be only vaguely approximate. So
why can we not be contented to think of our ancestors as having been here a very long time? We
mean of course a very long time for man as such—
because apparently he was a very late arrival on our
planet. Practically everything else in the way of
fauna and flora preceded him here, and his near relations (various species of the great ape group)
were scampering about in India and other eastern
countries ages before the creature known as man had
ever been developed.

But when he did finally make his entry upon life's
stage, he soon cast all allied rivals into the shade,
proceeded to occupy an ever-increasing share of his
local environment, and made himself generally feared
and disliked by the animal life in his immediate
vicinity. This he was able to accomplish because

actually he was a supermammal, even though his closest relatives were not very distinguished members of that great society. This strange being furthermore was apparently born with an ego, whatever exactly that might imply, and he certainly made good use of this peculiarity which was to prove one of his crowning assets in a world of rather unprogressive animal life. Ego, on its lower levels, is just another form of self-conscious introspection and something which betokens an awareness of one's personality. Under this strange influence, enhanced by ambition, the mind of man has been able to achieve extraordinary heights of intellectual endeavor during the centuries of his existence. But we must not infer that at the beginning of his career he possessed anything more than a mere suggestion of this precious quality. Indeed, in his earliest stages it might have been practically nonexistent.

It is difficult to estimate at just what period in his development our ancestor slipped across the line which distinguished him from the lower animals. Whether the transition occurred first in his mental capability or became evident in his physical attitude is also a point of great scientific interest. The mists of time so far have obscured the facts, but it may be that the conundrum will be solved in the near future.

The mental stimulus which man is assumed to have

experienced whenever in his career he stood erect
in his walking and running pose has been fully
stressed by numerous scientists. They argue that the
release of the forelegs as a means of progression as
well as a supporting factor, and their subsequent
use as arms and hands, gave to our early progenitors
a distinct physical superiority among a host of quadrupedal animals. For, combined with this advantage,
the lengthened opposable thumb could function in
a manner never before seen in a living creature. With
these new mechanisms, it appears that man could
more easily pick up and closely examine any object
that aroused his latent curiosity, and in this way he
greatly developed the power of concentration and
observation.

However, too much importance may be ascribed
to these anatomical changes, especially their effect
on the mental outlook, because it is quite evident to
any student that the chimpanzee, for example, very
often and with perfect ease *does* pick up and scruti-
nize any small object which attracts his attention—in
fact, it is a rather characteristic pose among the
higher primates. There can be no doubt, however,
that the opposable thumb imparted to man the
power to grasp with a firm grip and to hold an implement, a stick or a stone perhaps, which could be
used either as a weapon or for some more peaceful
purpose. This was a distinct asset to a creature liv-

ing in the midst of dangers and forced to make his own livelihood under adverse conditions; but it hardly accounts for his almost supernatural ability to take advantage of everything that contributed to his upward and progressive course of action in higher spheres of mental and physical activity.

When we consider that the orang, the chimpanzee, and the gorilla (or at least allied species) were in existence when man was first experiencing a higher phase of sensibility, the reasons for their retarded mental advancement, while living under practically the same physical conditions as those of early man, cannot be disregarded. If we return for a moment to a survey of our very early ancestors, we note that they are all tree-dwelling, or arboreal, forms. Lemurs, tree shrews, and tarsiers were distinctly creatures of the leafy branches—living and dying in their lofty retreats and finding food, and protection as well, far above the floor of the forest with all its dangers and frightening experiences. Certainly the chimpanzee and the gorilla are today very largely ground-living forms, though the orangs and gibbons still stick closely to a life in the treetops, where they seem to enjoy a rather peaceful and uneventful existence. It is true that both chimps and gorillas may ascend trees, but only under certain conditions, usually to obtain food or to escape from some ground-living enemy. But as a rule they do not actually *live* arboreally, preferring the ground-dwelling habitat because of their restless and energetic dispositions, and also very probably to extend their food range.

We know that gorillas in particular travel considerable distances every day in search of provender, but their gait in this very necessary perambulation is quadrupedal—that is, they amble about on all fours for most of their waking hours. Both chimps and gorillas have very long arms and short legs, and neither specie is able to stand upright and take a stride directly forward, as we do customarily when advancing over the ground. Anatomical differences between the ape's pelvic region and that of man prevent the ape from achieving this highly important function except in a very clumsy manner. Their method of getting about is a fast, one-sided shuffle on all fours, but not upon the flat of the hand. The fingers, bent at the first joint, carry the weight of the forepart of the body upon the heavily padded knuckles, while the very small thumb does not touch the ground as would our own in a similar pose. The hind limbs are short, so short in fact that the backline drops sharply from the hunched-up shoulders to the hips. The big toe of the hind foot is separated widely from the other four, more in the nature of a thumb than a toe, but the whole foot is placed flat upon the sod in truly manlike fashion. Should the animal be urged in any way, excited, angered or frightened, it moves quickly for a short distance in a semierect posture, barely touching its front feet to the earth. But it does not habitually maintain this attitude, nor does it *ever* stand erect and run in the fashion of a man.

This short description of the progression of a chimpanzee or a gorilla must have applied equally well to our early ancestors before the miracle of the upright gait became a part of our very being. Whenever, in man's history, he felt the insistent urge to stand in a vertical position, it almost seems as though some internal force must have persuaded him to do so. Even at an early age children are very determined to attain the erect stance, though they can at the same time walk about on all fours, but *not* with bent knuckles—the *flat* of their hands being placed upon the ground. The entire pose, however, becomes difficult and irksome at a time when the child's legs begin to grow definitely longer than his arms. So that, after all, it may have been only the lengthening of his legs, and not some occult force that caused man to stand upright and walk about in a way that was ever after to be one of his many unique peculiarities.

Thus it is that we may glimpse our early relative as he poses, perhaps with slightly stooped shoulders, upon the threshold of his newly acquired inheritance.

From now on he was to free himself from the four-legged clan to which he had belonged for millions of years and stride boldly forth to conquer the world. Naturally at the time he did not realize what lay before him in the extraordinary career to which, through no volition of his own, he had fallen heir. He knew only that he had to eat, to defend himself against wild beasts or others of his own species, to seek a mate, and to make himself as comfortable as possible under all conditions. The power to accomplish these things must have been inherent in his personality, but the plane of such desires and ambitions was, without his being aware of the fact, to be on a higher level than any ever accomplished in the entire field of living things. Whole vistas of a new phase of life stretched away before this lowly creature, yet at the time he could not visualize them or know that the hand of a great destiny was to fall upon those rough and hairy shoulders, urging him, guiding him, and finally disclosing to his retentive and highly intelligent mind strange and wonderful ideas of which he was to take full advantage in the ages to come. Indeed, there can be nothing to discourage the believer in man's final emancipation when he carefully considers this brief survey of his early existence. Rather, if one goes deeply into the matter, satisfaction is assured in the thought that, in spite of man's lowly lineage, he was able to break away from a purely animal condition into the realm of intellectual and spiritual predominance which he has ever since occupied.

We do not claim for the early human any great amount of physical beauty, for he was undoubtedly quite brutish in appearance; but we must always remember that he was never under par in any way, especially mentally. Rather was he extremely intelligent; more so, in fact, than any other creature in the entire world. By this very astuteness he was able to rise superior to physical surroundings in an always dangerous and difficult environment.

We must realize also that man in his newly erect state was not well fitted to cope with life's vicissitudes when compared to the carnivora of his day. For armed as they were with huge teeth and claws, he must have seemed a puny specimen indeed. His teeth were small, his muscles comparatively weak, and his power of resistance sadly inefficient whenever it came to battling with savage lionlike creatures, or prowling hyenas, ever on the watch to seize and devour him. In addition to these terrible marauders, there were others almost as dangerous: elephants, rhinoceros, hippopotami, buffalos and wild boars, pythons and crocodiles. Against this terrible array, our ancestor's physical strength was of little avail, and had that been his only method of defense, the chances for his survival would have been reduced to a minimum. Fortunately for his descendants, there existed within that rather drab and insignificant exterior a type of mentality apparently capable of surmounting and eventually conquering many of these difficulties. This superintelligence, combined with a highly adaptable physical constitution, was sufficient to insure a continued existence until such a time as he learned to arm himself with offensive and defensive weapons.

The world, as far as these early beings were concerned, must have been a small one—confined, in fact, to a strictly local environment. But at some time or other, as his mental equipment improved and became the dominating feature of existence, a certain realization and awareness of his position in such proscribed surroundings became ever more apparent. The human side of man's nature began to assert itself, and thoughts which had never assailed him in earlier days grew more insistent and troublesome under the urge of a newly developed personality.

No longer was he content merely to eat, to sleep, to propagate, and to sit idly about gazing with unseeing eyes at the local scenery. For now man had constructive ideas. He *wanted* things, and if his neighbors had a specially comfortable shelter in which to hide at night, envious thoughts arose and at times he was able to drive them out of the coveted retreat and occupy it himself. How little could ancient man have realized the terrible potentialities inherent in *that* train of thought, and how in later ages it was to become the curse of the world!

If man had always remained an unarmed brute, the mere desire to seize and hold a certain place, or piece of ground, or a soft nest at the root of some great tree might have been disagreeable for the ousted tenants, whether beings like himself or some more formidable animal. But no great damage was done to either participant in the scramble for the acquisition of a domicile. A bitten ear, a strained ankle, perhaps a bruised shoulder were the worst results of such an encounter.

We must not infer, however, that because man held within himself great possibilities for mental advancement he had risen superior to all the long-established traits and characteristics of his animal ancestors. On the contrary he retained many of these traits, both good and bad. To them he added numerous sinister and distinctly more human attributes which later became somewhat of an obsession in his more or less primitive mind. To the basic emotions of fear, hunger and anger, he learned to react in a manner governed by a new technique. His conscious self, aided by an increased reasoning power, made him cunning, resourceful, and more self-reliant.

There was less reason for panic because he could better foresee and forestall impending trouble, and he also learned to play, to invent, and to take advantage of favorable circumstances for his own betterment and protection.

The ability to sit and ruminate, to recollect and to learn by experience and imitation gave him a tremendous advantage over his less fortunate adversaries, but his existence was, at the same time, to be vastly complicated by new sets of emotions. The mere fact of living, a comparatively simple affair in his earlier history, had become a somewhat annoying condition under his greatly sensitized nervous development, and he may even in those early times have suffered from fits of depression.

Hungry he had always been, but in some miraculous way at least enough food was provided to keep him from starvation. Though his teeth do not indicate a meat diet, for ages the flesh of animals has been a favorite with members of the human stock, even though roots, fruits, grubs, and birds' eggs were much more easily procured. As an animal, these simple viands had been quite sufficient to stave off hunger pangs, but when manlike aspirations evidenced themselves in his character, such lowly hunger-appeasers grew less important in his daily thoughts. Visions of feasts on actual animal food became a habit with our at one time vegetarian ancestor.

In the old days he had gazed greedily at some plump little deer, or tried, usually without success, to seize a perching bird on a low-lying tree branch. In his new role, he was gradually to realize that with the aid of the simplest of weapons—a stick or a stone —he might be able to kill such small game. Other things too, now that he had grasped the original idea, could be readily disposed of in the same way. How easy it was to sneak up on an enemy in a neighboring clan in the dense jungle and tap him none too gently on his thick skull with a heavy club or a piece of sharp stone! To be sure, the other fellow might be equally well armed and fight back, but he had to take his chances on that, and so whenever he went deep into the forest fortresses it behooved him to stop, look, and listen to the best of his ability.

Man must always have been an expert in forest lore, but now as an armed savage he became a scourge to the animal life about him as well as a menace to others of his own species whenever opportunity offered. It may have taken thousands of years for man to have advanced much further in his discovery and construction of offensive and defensive weapons, but his various migrations and above all changes in climatic conditions were a constant and even necessary stimulus to his already well-developed urge to kill and to destroy, both for food or to gain ascendance over his enemies. Under these circumstances, it was only a question of time before we observe that the broken branch was cut or burned to a sharp point with the result that the spear became finally a most important weapon, quite capable, in strong skilled hands, of doing terrible damage to an adversary, either man or beast. It was the spear in fact that long before the invention of the bow and arrow gave to man the power to wound and kill very large game animals, as well as the means of annihilating objectionable individuals of his own species. These latter obstructions to the attainment of his personal ends were regarded with small favor by our old-time relative, and we may rest assured his neighbors viewed him in exactly the same way. We have no doubt that it often became a question of who was who in the jungle retreats, and that fierce battles were the result of any chance meetings between our unsavory antecedents when tribal or family differences were involved.

The question of sex and the selection of a mate was a difficult problem for ancient man, especially after he had learned the use of weapons. We have no way of knowing whether he had one or several members of the opposite sex as companions in his adult existence, but it is quite probable that he was polygamous as are the gorillas and chimpanzees of the present day. There seems to be no general rule which governs the number of females which associate, either temporarily or permanently, with the male animal of any species. In many types there is a separation of the sexes after the breeding period is over for the season. In others, and the gorilla seems to belong in this category, the small family, consisting of the old male, a female or two, perhaps a couple of yearling young and a half-grown male or female, will travel about together in an amicable manner. But just as soon as a young male reaches maturity he either leaves the family group of his own accord or is driven out by the original fully adult male parent.

We may imagine that early man went through a very similar course of action, but after his adoption of a weapon or two, his field of aggression became much enlarged and he may easily have coveted a female from some neighboring tribe or clan. There was trouble ahead for him in this idea, but man has always been looking for trouble since his early inception, and so our lowly hero, nothing daunted, proceeded to risk his life for what appeared to him to be something very desirable. There was nothing chivalrous or sentimental in his attitude, for he was merely answering nature's call, as has every other created being since life began. In the case of our ancestor, however, nature was assisted by a trusty pointed stick or spear, a knobby club, and a sharp stone, all to be used against stubborn rivals who might be expected to give as good as they received in a quick scrimmage around and between forest trees, or over rough and rocky ground in more open country. If successful in his foray, the female thus secured was brought back into the man's family fold or the pair began a new life of their own within the general community. Other women could be added to the family if desirable, and so the clans and small tribes grew apace. No longer was man a solitary creature eking out a lonely existence and only casually meeting the opposite sex at intervals which varied as opportunity offered. He had at length become a gregarious animal, thereby immensely strengthening his power of resistance and his aggressive force against any and all types of adversaries.

The agelong propensity of man for desiring and acquiring things which did not really belong to him was not satisfied entirely by securing a much-prized female, important as that feat of arms undoubtedly proved to be. For our ancestor, true to his early inheritance from the lemur-tree-shrew constituency, was at heart a thief, and played true to type on all favorable occasions. With his supermentality always at work, the fun of planning raids, scheming for the precise moment of attack, and the sharpening of his spears and stone weapons were mere pastimes for that devilish little brain to work upon. Indeed we may be sure that our grubby relative was no model specimen of humanity, and while the picture is not a pretty one, it must be very close to the truth. However, we really can't blame man for his shortcomings because he, like everything else on earth, had absolutely nothing to say about his appearance here, nor the reasons for his existence. He led the only mode of life that seemed to suit his special needs and aspirations. Quite unconcerned about his past or his future, he played the role of a highly gifted animal in all his activities, and was deeply engrossed in saving himself from oblivion. If there was anything supernatural about him, he certainly did not know it. Nevertheless, we who now regard him from the higher plane of much more recent intelligence, *can* distinguish certain things in his unique character which bear the stamp of an extraordinary originality. Those were the subtle differences of behavior, and reaction to exterior and interior influences, that were to govern this strange creature through all the long years of his adolescence and pristine manhood.

In recent years it has been surmised, and not without logic, that early man may have been derived from not one, but several, primitive stocks. The recent finds in South Africa and Java would appear to confirm the idea that our ancestral tree had its roots in widely separated areas of the earth's surface and that these earlier species could have differed somewhat in general appearance as a result of varying environment. Conclusions about this point, however, should be anything but final because at present the relative antiquity of these finds is very much in doubt.

On the evidence of the skeletal material, the South African discoveries seem vastly more primitive than the Java fossils, but the geological time of the African types has thus far not been ascertained; and, of course, we do not believe that all varieties of early man necessarily erupted at the same time from their still earlier quadrupedal state into the form of our erect-walking progenitors.

Today the local habitats of these two discoveries are widely different, the Java region being truly tropical with much rain and humidity, while the South African field is high, dry, and semiarid in climate. This does not mean necessarily that similar conditions existed when the two primitive man types were alive, because hundreds of thousands of years have intervened since then, and we know how greatly the climate and the geographical and geological aspects of the world can be influenced in the course of ages.

So far in the progress of our story we have spoken of man only in the most general way, but as he was after all a personality and continually becoming more definitely a human being like ourselves, the impact of outside conditions both physical and mental must be considered. Man has been reviewed very casually, first as an animal, then as a primitive human offshoot from that type, and finally under the stress of growing emotions and basic urges. His capabilities for advancement have been demonstrated to a certain extent. Whether during this part of his history man was more than dimly conscious of his environment, noticed heat or cold, was placid or nervous, is only to be judged at this late day by a comparison with his nearest living relatives, the great apes of the old world. Even this comparison will not quite explain man's feelings during the earlier stages of his history, because of his superior sensibilities even during those extremely ancient periods.

When today one of the big apes feels cold, he crawls into a hole in a tree trunk or makes a rough bed of leaves in which he finds passable protection. There is no doubt that man as a mere mammal had to be content with a primitive type of shelter, but his change of heart and mind made him restless and uncomfortable under conditions once accepted as inevitable. The still-prevalent idea among certain types of people that Mother Nature is a benevolent old lady, looking carefully after the welfare of her beloved offspring, is not borne out by a study of the actual facts. Early man, we may be sure, had his full share of troubles and anxieties with very little assistance, if any, from sources other than his own superior wits and physical adaptabilities. We have already indicated a few of his fast-growing troubles and aspirations, but certainly more complex and nerve-

shattering experiences were in store for him as his
mental sagacity increased. He was able to circumvent
many of these troubles, while it seemed quite beyond
his earthly powers to avoid or to anticipate others.
Climate, with its vicissitudes and unpredictable qualities, was an ever-increasing element in man's life
struggle, and because of his comparatively weak
physical stamina, we are not surprised that so far
his very early remains have been found only in warm
countries. Clad in the garb in which nature fashioned
him, anything like the chilly regions which he later
was able to occupy would have been impossible.

The tropical and semitropical regions of South
Africa, India, South China, and the Islands of the
Malay Peninsula all exhibited, at some time or
other, degrees of climate favorable to man's early
growth and development as well as those of his
fellow primates—chimps, orangs, gorillas, and his
still more remote and earlier relatives. Certainly at
the beginning of man's existence he could have been
mentally only a few steps ahead of his nearest
cousins; but even then that uncanny quality in his
make-up prompted him to think hard over his difficulties. The overcoming of climatic extremes was
undoubtedly one of them. When it rained in tor-
rents, he naturally sought shelter under leaves and
branches, or in hollow trees or caves if such natural
excavations were handy. These were, of course,

purely animal reactions and instinctive in all land-living creatures.

Even in those early times, however, we like to think of man as something more than a mere mammal, so that as time went on, he may have mulled over the possibility of constructing some sort of a shelter from the elements, something to help keep the rain off his bushy head and the rest of his meager anatomy. It wasn't a very bright idea because even the orang had thought of that expediency. Man's shelter, however, was a clumsy affair, and not improved upon in any way as the years passed. On the contrary when it came to use of his clever brain and nimble fingers, ultimately he learned to weave great leaves together into a kind of thatched roof and to support the structure by placing broken saplings under it, their ends stuck into the ground. The finished product must have been pretty homely; small, without sides, and only partially effective, yet it *was* a shelter, albeit a most primitive one, and it presaged great things in the ages to come. Of greater significance, it was something no other mammal had ever erected against the elements.

There is something pathetic and prophetic in the lonely forest scene as we contemplate man's first abode, created by his own hands, actuated by his feeble but still superior brain. The green and dripping trees rise high above the tiny dwelling, while under it crouches a little family of our ancestors, arms wrapped about each other's shivering torsos— dreary and insignificant nobodies in the vast reaches of their tropical environment. It is with difficulty that we recognize these lowly creatures as the progenitors of a species which in future ages would create gigantic structures of brick, stone and steel, attesting to man's power, resourcefulness, and determination to dominate the world. Moreover, we become aware of an outstanding trait in man's character: his restless and far-reaching determination not to be content with conditions as he finds them, but to supplement these conditions with creations of his own making, in an effort to improve any given set of circumstances when he feels that they do not contribute satisfactorily to his ideas and general welfare. For man, we must admit, is unique mentally, and has always pursued his own peculiar way through the long ages of his tempestuous career. Had it not been so, no leafy little hut would ever have arisen to stave off the elements from his sensitive skin, and we might still be living off fruits and nuts in the midst of a tropical jungle. We shall therefore regard the tiny first house as a symbol, a vision of things to come. It proves the presence of an inner force quite beyond our understanding.

Time was to multiply these fragile habitations and to make them, by the addition of sides and a tiny entrance, into an actual hut, perhaps much in the form of the dwelling places used by certain African pygmies to this very day. At any rate, these strange old-time beings had, by this apparently simple, but actually most complicated and revolutionary line of action, proved that they possessed minds filled with original and amazing ideas stowed away in their flat little craniums. We have no way of knowing just what line of mental activity came first into the mind of ancient man, and the constructed shelter is used merely as an illustration of what he must have attempted when opportunity offered.

In a more sterile and rocky country he, with all sorts of other mammals, a few types of bird and still lowlier forms, regarded the rock shelters or actual caves with favorable eyes. It was a perfect retreat for early man who, by the simple process of piling up a heap of stones and brush at the entrance, could make an effectual barrier against the inroads of wild beasts or other undesirable marauders of his own species. The extreme importance of cave deposits in the study of fossil men and animals will be considered more fully in later chapters, but here it is enough to imagine with what alacrity our progenitors dived into these friendly shelters at the least sign of danger, or whenever the weather conditions became insupportable in the open.

Returning briefly to our early jungle domiciles,

the arboreal propensities inherited from our very
early tree-living ancestors were not by any means
forgotten, so that at least temporary living quarters
might have been constructed among the branches
of some great trees. In time of danger, a high perch
or a convenient limb was not to be sneered at, because comparatively few big carnivora could climb
the vertical trunk, and with the exception of such
dangerous killers as the leopardlike cats, man could
rest safely in his leafy abode.

Even to this day he is a good climber, and a boy
or young man accustomed to the task can get about
in search of fruits or honey or birds' eggs in a manner
quite astonishing to the ordinary observer. We are,
however, so accustomed to our two-legged means
of progression that our tree-climbing powers are
cast completely into the shade by the nimbleness of
numerous other species of mammals. Among these
the great apes, and more especially the gibbons and
the smaller monkeys, can dash about from branch
to branch, jumping, swinging across open spaces from
tree to tree, and displaying their abilities generally
in an astonishing and convincing manner. Whenever we are treated to one of these surpassing exhibitions of physical agility, it becomes apparent that
man today has come a long way from his original
tree-dwelling propensities, and that for many ages
past, his true home has been a terrestrial affair.

The comparative austerity of this form of existence was taken for granted by our ancestors, who found themselves in an environment under which rather simple living conditions persisted with scant changes or improvements until man began those long and far-reaching migrations so characteristic of his later history. He was then to discover that though leafy abodes served his purpose admirably while he lived in warm and salubrious surroundings, they were far from adequate in the colder climates which he was to encounter in his progress northward and westward from his original home. At any rate, he had made a good beginning toward the solution of his housing problem when we picture him beneath a leaf-thatched little domain in the midst of some luxuriant forest retreat.

Even in his early stages, things must have been distinctly favorable to his development so that we see him growing ever more competent both physically and mentally, stronger, better fed, and far more able to look after himself and his family. The procurement of sufficient food was, of course, always the primary necessity in his day-to-day existence. Shelter, while desirable, could be dispensed with at times, but the emotion of fear, a purely mental attribute, remained a substantial bugaboo, cramping and yet stimulating in its influence upon his personality. Pleasure, as we know it, could have been only vaguely comprehended, and the satisfaction of a full stomach or a successful raid upon a neighboring community quite filled the bill for our hirsute kinsman in the heyday of his primitive existence.

Without doubt the curious trait of man's restless ambition was in great part responsible for his sensational advancement in a world of more static animal forms, because without effort no progress seems possible to any living creature. Nevertheless, the amazing speed with which man developed his conceptions from those of the brute into the highly sensitized realm of thought later reflected in his every action is something which we are presently unable to comprehend. As a creature he appears to have been stimulated from within by the urge of an insatiable ambition to accomplish definite results, to surpass and even to destroy if necessary any and all rivals to his predominance in personal and tribal affairs. The greatness of the role man was to play in the making of world history must have been of small moment to our ancestral brotherhood who reckoned only his small requirements and desires as of importance in the scheme of living. But the spirit of adventure, the wanderlust, and the intense desire to be somewhere other than the particular place which he occupied at the moment were also very much a part of man's inherent characteristics. This being the case, it becomes evident that no one spot, however favorable for living it might prove to be, could long suit our moderately intelligent but tremendously virile relatives.

Dreams of conquest, however limited, were even then part of man's intellectual equipment, but to gain advantage over one's enemies required weapons, and the tools with which to fashion those spears and knives and other types of aggressive implements. Stones too could be employed in a variety of ways and, broken to a sharp edge or point, they served to cut flesh or to remove the meat from a dead animal. As hammers, nothing served better than a heavy stone to pound or crack a bone for the marrow, while the crushing of a big fruit or nut was an easy matter with the force of the blow greatly augmented by a great rock grasped in a powerful hand.

In this connection it is always well to remember that whenever man and his works are under discussion, it is necessary to realize a certain correlation in all his efforts. Owing to his powerful imagination and definite reasoning qualities, one thing led automatically to another in all his various activities, social or otherwise. His physical necessities for living and the carrying out of his desires rose on a constantly ascending scale as his self-confidence and intelligence increased. Dangers of every sort could and had to be met and overcome with the aid of superior weapons, for no other creature except those of his own species had the intelligence to create these formidable additions to their fighting equipment.

Therefore he had to devote a great part of his time to the manufacture of offensive and defensive weapons. Life under such adverse conditions was certainly no bed of roses, but required great resourcefulness and vigilance on the part of our much harassed forebears. The prospect, however, seems not to have daunted the fiery little brutes who somehow continued to thrive, develop, and multiply, and gradually in the course of time to wander far afield from their original dwelling places.

New hunting grounds, new adventures, and even difficult weather and living conditions all acted as a tonic to the curiously nomadic strain in man's inner nature. We are not prepared to explain this extraordinary urge to seek new fields for living. We only know that our ancient progenitors were always determined to progress, often blindly, but none the less successfully. Naturally there were other reasons for the development of the migratory instinct in the races of early man. The lack of sufficient food in a given locality would have presented a powerful incentive for a change to a better-stocked section of country, while the too near presence of hostile and powerful neighbors, an epidemic of disease or some great natural catastrophe such as a violent volcanic eruption, a great earthquake, or a tremendous flood are additional possible causes for leaving the places of origin. All these devastating influences, however, do not account for the constant desire for a change of scene so evident in man's history, nor for the very great distances which he was able to negotiate in the course of time.

In those distant days our world was certainly not overcrowded with humanity as is the case at present. Vast numbers of animals of every sort and kind roamed the forests or the open country in all parts of the various continents. The food problem, therefore, could never have been more than local, especially in the favored regions wherein our antique relations have left evidences of their early occupancy. We cannot conceive of a reason for the great movement northward and westward which apparently became a sort of *idée fixe* among our prehistoric ancestors, especially since in those directions lay great unknown, inhospitable regions which eventually grew more bleak, cold, and depressing as the climates in many parts of the world changed under the influence of the glacial periods in geologic history.

The question of man's antiquity, and by this we mean his actual first appearance as a pseudo-human type, presents a problem not easily solved. The sites of his former abode in this very early phase of his existence are not many and their geological age is difficult to determine. They do, however, vastly amplify the time period for man's upgrowing stages, a few thousand years at the most being quite as far back as the early chronicles dare to imagine. Now we know that in the precise shape and physical guise of modern man we have skeletal remains perhaps 30,000 years old, and this veritable modern type came from somewhere in eastern Europe at a still earlier time.

Going back for a moment to the earliest known manlike creatures so far discovered, those of the *Plesianthropus,* a South African species, the estimates are so varied that it is difficult to state with any degree of certainty the remoteness of this fossil creature. However, we can truthfully say that the specimens must be several hundred thousand years old, perhaps 500,000, possibly more. With this we may compare the Java fossil, *Pithecanthropus,* also a very old type, as having lived a matter of 300,000 years in the deep past. Should these larger estimates of the length of man's sojourn here be approximately correct, they will not detract from the amazing speed with which man as man, though a very primitive one, was able to develop his astounding mentality and at the same time assume the commanding position of dominance which he has now held for many thousands of years.

Nevertheless, we must appreciate that a rather slow progression at first (and by this we mean the long ages of his adjustment and evolution from the anthropoid type) occupied a large proportion of man's early history, and that he did not come into his own realm of extreme superiority as a species until possibly some 60,000 years ago. We have also regarded him as a forest-loving creature, which he probably was in his earlier years; but according to recent ideas upon the subject, forest denizens tend not to advance mentally, and remain in a rather somnolent condition as far as progress is concerned. So it is that we should come to expect ancient man's emergence from a forest environment at a fairly early period of his career.

It is to his credit that he essayed a life in the open because such an existence was distinctly at variance with his experiences as a woods-dweller. Apparently the circumscribed nature of his ancient home began at length to pall upon our ambitious antecedents, and man emerged at long last from the woods both literally and figuratively into the great open spaces. A wholly new life awaited him here beneath the open sky. Such a region infused new energy into our doughty relative. He wanted to run, to hunt big game, to wander afield, and generally to extend his entire outlook. He had by now become more independent, more aggressive, and more resourceful. He may have learned to trap big game by the use of pitfalls. Horses, antelopes, cattle all could have fallen into a well-concealed hole dug in some much-used game trail. Fishing of a kind could have been indulged in for another variety of food. Small nets made from vines pocketed the finny prey in shallow water where they were easily captured with bare hands and thrown upon the stream bank. Birds were probably netted too, or struck down with a light stick; and lizards and snakes were very plentiful and easily secured.

Thus far we have seen man creeping cautiously through jungle lanes, hiding in the underbrush or behind trees as the coveted quarry approached. In open country such tactics were impossible, so that speed and stamina for a long chase became prime requisites for our lowly nimrods. If man was not at first a fast long-distance runner, he soon became so because his very life often depended upon the agility with which he could avoid the charge of an infuriated animal, or dash after a sorely stricken deer or antelope. In open country no closely set tree trunks warded off the attacks of either man or beast, and no sheltering bushes hid him from view. All in all, it was a strenuous and exciting existence, a kind of life that called for the best that was in man's character, but as usual, he was apparently equal to its constant vicissitudes. Better weapons were a necessity under these conditions, and a sharpened bone or piece of broken stone lashed to the top of his wooden spear

Pithecanthropus and orang meet in the Java jungle

Peking man and woolly rhinoceros in a death struggle

shaft made a really formidable type of killing implement. In skillful hands such a contrivance even today
will produce a dangerous killer. Then it was a struggle for existence, and only the stronger and more
determined hunters could hope to survive.

Whatever may have been the social state of early
man, whether fairly solitary or gregarious (and we
have suggested the latter as the more probable), he
undoubtedly became more gregarious as time went
on, either for convenience or protection or both. He
did finally adopt the clan or even tribal state of culture as being especially suited to his personal needs,
desires, and inclinations. Within these primal aggre-
gations, the spirit of emulation, jealousy, and ambition (even though these emotions were as yet in a
primitive stage) naturally began to assert itself. Yet
we cannot ignore the fact that, in spite of conflicting
forces and personalities, the gregarious state was a
tremendous help in shaping man's future course for
his long journey up the mountain of his physical
and dawning spiritual consciousness. Freedom from
continual persecution, food in more constant quantities, and the comfort of association with his fellow
beings could prove only highly beneficial factors in
man's progressing history. Coupled with these advantages was the profound force of selection now given
full play by the stimulus of competition among certain tribal members in various physical and mental

activities and accomplishments. There was sure to be some individual in every clan who either excelled in the making of weapons or could outfight or out-run anyone else in the community. He, we may be sure, would be favored by the females, or picked to lead a foray against a neighboring tribe. The law of selection would underlie these primitive emotions, but the results would be beneficial to the band as a whole.

At what particular stage of his career ancient man learned to produce fire, we have no sure way of knowing. He undoubtedly was conscious of its exist-ence from his earliest conception, an emotion natu-rally shared by practically all species of higher living creatures. Fear and revulsion were the primeval and spontaneous reactions to this strange and mysterious element whose hot breath could scorch and destroy everything in its path. The fantastic phenomenon of flame, which materialized before one's very eyes and brought results so dire that they were evident to even the most limited mind, could only have struck terror to the senses of our untutored progenitors. To the modern intelligence the underlying reasons for com-bustion are no longer a closed book, but we can readily imagine the terrible shock sustained by all earlier conscious beings in the presence of the great destroyer. Lightning flashes, forest and grass fires, volcanos belching forth sparks, smoke, flames, and

glowing rivulets of lava coursing down the mountain-
side—all these fearful spectacles were well within
the experiences of early man, whose one and only
course of action under such frightening conditions
was to flee, if indeed flight were possible. No wonder
then, that the ancient savage was terrorized at the
sight of fire and that annihilation did, in reality,
descend upon many of our long-distant relations,
strive as they did to escape the all-devouring element.

But fortunately for the human race, man's fertile
and ever-watchful mental perceptions came to his
aid in the eventual taming of fire for his own uses
and to his great advantage. He noticed perhaps that
a grateful warmth bathed his chilly, naked body at
some time when he had ventured near the smoldering
trunk of a tree, or that the wild pig, killed by the
pursuing flames of a grass fire, had proved a toothsome morsel for a ravenous appetite. These were
no doubt welcome discoveries to our always hungry
ancestor, but he was to go still further eventually
and produce fire himself whenever and wherever he
desired it. For now our growing prodigy was beginning to notice many things and to put two and
two together in a most astonishing way. Processes
and results of fires of which he had taken no account
in his early youth, became ever more apparent to
his developing mental capacity. We are not surprised,
therefore, to see him at length producing a tiny flame

in a dry piece of wood by the friction of another piece of wood against its desiccated surface, and augmenting that flame with some moss or wood fiber held closely against the burning tinder. Again, he could have watched the sparks fly from the heavy impact of one hard stone upon another and seen how the dried grass around the sparks burst into flame. We need not speculate about them, remote as their first developments may be, because man simply had, at one time, to observe these phenomena and to take advantage of them cleverly and permanently. Of course, man didn't know and couldn't have conceived of the great boon these apparently simple natural forces would later prove to be in his struggle for existence, nor the tremendous part that his knowledge of the use of fire was to play in the future activities of his descendants.

Fortunately for present-day man, the ancient types were possessed of a very keen appreciation of new thoughts and conceptions, a quality of character not particularly apparent in the lower animals. The less gifted types of mammals were shy on ideas except in a most hazy and futile way, and for that reason they remained in a more or less inert state mentally, while man, their contemporary, was steadily climbing the heights dictated by his superintelligent mind. So it was that once the use of fire became more or less commonplace among the tribes of ancient man, he straightway began to cook his meat and fish and parch the grain or nuts that his womenfolk gathered in their wanderings. Early man appreciated too the pleasant sensation of heat against chilled, naked bodies and slept more peacefully at night because of fire's frightening influence upon all sorts of nocturnal marauders—wolves, hyenas, lions, and even malicious human enemies. Then as now the blazing logs held a curious fascination for members of the human species, so that when the tribal chiefs and elders decided to palaver with each other, and by means of signs or perhaps intelligible grunts to communicate ideas, the fire hearth became a central focus for all such important events. The world in general has benefited tremendously by the use of this extraordinary element, but it has also suffered untold hardships, death, and terrible destruction from the same source. Tamed and controlled, we may look upon its manifold uses with satisfaction, but unchecked it still remains the dreaded enemy of all life.

Early man was, like every other animated being, at times a victim of violent volcanic action, forest fires, lightning, and all other primal forces operating in that distant period in precisely the manner that they do today. To a less courageous soul the difficulties and dangers of those days, of which man was an unwilling victim, would have appeared impossible to surmount, or even to resist successfully. But our

old-time relative was a very tough and resilient type
of human being—a fighter, an opportunist, and a
most consistent optimist. Whether he lacked the
brains to be otherwise or was the happy possessor
of an iron-clad nervous system, we shall never know.
At any rate he contrived to weather all his difficulties,
and these must have increased tremendously whenever he essayed any migrations from his original
home acres, wandering for seemingly impossible distances. Naturally, these long journeys didn't happen
overnight. There were no airplanes, trains, busses, or
steamships to serve the restless little fellow. Nor
were there any comforts ready at his hand, no matter
which way he turned in a decidedly inhospitable
world.

Geographic conditions, severe changes in climate,
new and dangerous wild animals were alike ar-
rayed against these early adventurers who, nothing
daunted, continued their travels in different eras of
geologic time, through Asia, Africa, Europe, and
the great islands of the Pacific. Naturally all these
vast areas changed greatly through the hundreds of
thousands of years of man's long journeys. The
Pacific islands—Java, Sumatra, Borneo, and others
—weren't always islands. Indeed, at one time they
were a part of the Asiatic Mainland. The climates
of all those vast regions must have changed too in
the course of time, growing colder, warmer, drier,

or more humid by turns; while man, miserable but indomitable man, persisted through it all.

There were various species of great apes in existence long before the peculiarly manlike types had developed. It was that curious combination of mental and physical characteristics which eventually separated man so completely from his original racial stock. We are, of course, not completely sure that the ape of any species will prove to be the direct ancestor of the human race, but we do know with certainty at present that both man and primate (perhaps in the shape and physiognomy of a female chimpanzee) must have closely resembled each other in general appearance, although the ape still continued to walk on all fours while our emancipated relatives had already risen to the erect posture of a man. It is possible, and indeed probable, that the ape family, coincident with the early appearance of man, has advanced considerably through long periods in both physical and mental capacity. But how meager these laboriously acquired advantages appear when compared to the marvelous truth of man's steady and outstanding evolution into a higher realm of mental consciousness. We see him even at this early date, high upon the slopes of his unique mental elevation, outstripping with ease and assurance all other animal types in resourcefulness and in ability of an entirely new order. He was still, to be sure, in a savage, primitive state of being, but his eyes seemed always fixed upon the attainment of every advantage that nature could bestow.

The animal world could not explain, and therefore feared, this two-legged, upright-walking braggart, nor can we ourselves understand just how or when the profound transformation occurred. Indeed, the situation even in those far-off days was more than passing strange because there seems to have been some deep and powerful force always at work to raise him ever higher upon his mountain of desire, and to renounce forever the valleys of his days of infancy. He could now look up to heights which he might never surmount.

On the other hand, we may be quite wrong in our assumption that early man had any ambition at all, or that his imagination was then of a very high order. He did have, nevertheless, some inkling of things other than his own immediate surroundings, and we know that in time he became a worshiper of natural forces—fire, water, wind, weather, and many other manifestations which he could not understand. In this distant period also, the probabilities of his experiencing any spiritual leanings or aspirations were nil. But the mere fact that he was observant enough to notice his surroundings presaged a high mental insight into things material, while the creating in his imagination of some appreciation of nature's presence—something outside of and superior to his own personality—at least indicated a leaning in the direction of things mystical and mysterious. We are safe in assuming that no great apes ever thought along these lines, nor can they do so at the present day. This peculiar form of intelligence, this stirring of the inner man and appreciation of something supernatural, is manifestly unique in our family and will partially explain all of our earlier and completely untutored proclivities towards a higher mental plane of living.

It was not a far cry, in the imagination of a primitive being intrigued by life's mysteries, to the realm of idolatry, which man began to practice somewhere along in his career. This type of worship, the bowing down to idols of wood, stone, or brass, is a form of religious emotion long regarded by peoples of the Christian faith with a peculiar horror and loathing. The word "heathen" is after all easily understood if one doesn't grow too emotional about it. Even today when communications are so readily made with distant lands, there remain many human beings who have not yet abandoned idolatry. Of course, the followers of Mohammed loom large in the world by sheer force of numbers, and there are Chinese, Japanese, and other great and powerful races of mankind, who maintain their own ideals and teachings in religious procedure, quite oblivious to our own Christian form of spiritual beliefs. Added to these, we have great numbers of primitive peoples, in Australia, Africa, and South America especially, who not only have failed to adopt any religion but, wonder of wonders, are still in the stone age of cultural development.

It should not, then, be a matter of amazement to realize that ancient man simply and sincerely learned to revere and regard as sacrosanct the dumb images of animals, human beings, or natural forces embodied in some special human representations which were thought to possess the powers of storm, fire, water, earthquake, or other dire and destructive elements inimical to man's happiness and peace of mind. On the contrary, the very desire, so evident in our ancient relatives, to consider such abstruse subjects as a necessary part of their sojourn here is a most extraordinary evidence of man's growing intellectual capacities—traits of inner character separating him further and further from anything but physical similarities with his primate relatives. We are not here speaking of man, at this early period of his abilities, as a being of any very grandiose conceptions, either physical, emotional, or spiritual. Indeed, we may be sure that he was a pretty rough customer, inured to privation and danger, or else he could never have survived the constant hard knocks which fate meted out to him on every possible occasion. No wonder, then, that in his more introspective moments he turned to idol worship as a help and guide on the long and dangerous road of his unsought destiny. Surely we must bear with our beleaguered ancestor in the midst of all his troubles and never condemn his often childish and inept struggles to raise himself above the many dangers which threatened not only his peace of mind, but his physical existence as well.

While mystical help no doubt proved some compensation to what was evidently a difficult scheme of living, ancient man at the same time possessed a very practical mind. He knew danger when he saw it, and he realized that no matter how strong and beneficent his particular sacred impersonation, it didn't altogether take the place of a good spear, a stone axe, or a well-made club or bone knife. Strenuous situations were by no means things of the past, and weapons, no matter how well made, could be broken, lost, or stolen at what might prove to be a crucial time. Weapons in general, and superior weapons in particular, called for expert manufacture, so that as soon as the clan idea became a permanent part of man's heritage there was a constant demand for especially skilled individuals who possessed the extra ability and finesse essential for the production of fighting implements.

We see, as time goes on, how the ancient and

original sharpened-stick spear gave way to a better made and more effective weapon in the shape of the bone or stone-tipped spear point fastened firmly to a long and powerful shaft of wood; and again the roughly broken or even natural nodule of flint had great possibilities for improvement in its evolution towards the beautifully shaped spear and arrow points of a later age. Our progenitors then, way back in the mists of time, lived a kind of double life, much as we, their descendants, do today. With one hand on the spear, early man inclined his head in some form of spirit worship, but apparently he realized even then that too much confidence could not be placed in a merely mental exaltation as a means of relief, and that he couldn't afford for a moment to relinquish his grasp on a physical weapon of some sort just as a matter of precaution. Human nature, we fear, has not changed greatly since those early mists obscured our newly created and inauspicious beginning.

Apparently man has always been a fighter, though not a particularly dangerous one until the time when he was able to make a spear or grasp a heavy stone. But on the day that he rose from his quadrupedal attitude to assume the erect carriage of a man, he became a potential killer. The powerful grasping hands, once used as forefeet, were then free to get him into all kinds of mischief. The opposable

thumb, one sign of man's changing anatomical construction, coupled with his walking and running ability and backed by a clever brain, made personal or
tribal supremacy a matter of the utmost importance
in man's social economy. Fighting prowess was to
be held at a premium, and a man blessed with superior physical stamina combined with force of character might in time become a leader or chief of his
clan or tribe.

The story of the struggle for supremacy was not
new to the world of animal creation where birds and
beasts had long battled others of their own species
as well as hostile marauders of other types which
sought to destroy them. Sex problems, the selection
of mates, and defense of the young were all fundamental characteristics of the world of life and very
important to the continuance of any race of animated
beings. Man, true to his mammalian affinities, could
only hope to carry on these crucial assignments even
though he was obliged to do so in his own particular manner.

In later and more specific chapters, the actual
discoveries of early man in various parts of the world
will receive more detailed attention, but the profound significance of man's appearance on this earth,
and his unique powers for development must always
remain the outstanding feature of any treatise on
his life history. How the subtle and sinister invader

made his entry so quietly into the realm of actuality and how his remarkable personality at a later day influenced even the secret and terrible forces which govern our universe are surely some of earth's great mysteries. Old Mother Nature little guessed the future of that serpent in her venerable bosom, nor how the child prodigy would one day overrun her great domain, destroying, altering, and finally mastering so many of her well-guarded secrets! We have already spoken of the fallacy that a kindly hand guided and watched over the lives of all living creatures. The facts show that a bitter struggle for supremacy has been going on ever since our old world was created. Into this entrenched and hostile environment our weak and futile ancestors were introduced and left to make their strenuous way as best they could, aided by nothing but their own initiative and determination to survive. To learn how well they succeeded we need only recapitulate man's long record of development, evolution, and conquest which, like the ripples from a stone dropped into the water, have spread in ever-widening circles until they encompassed the world. He was, however, not to be exempt from the difficulties and dangers which beset all life upon our planet, especially as he persisted through the ages in continually seeking new and distant fields of adventure and advancement.

The gradual flowering of a mentality and an ambition which apparently knew no bounds should be for us a lesson and a guide in its effects upon our own conduct here. For we are, it must be remembered, the children's children of these ancient wanderers, and at heart we have not changed in a surprisingly large number of their important and fundamental reactions, nor turned from the lines of conduct which they unconsciously pursued.

Our very general survey of man as an ancient type has brought him to a kind of milestone in his life story. The once brutelike creature has been traced through long ages of slow development to a period wherein he has acquired a certain kind of almost obligatory culture, which, though still in its primitive stage, definitely sets off our ancestor from his earlier apelike habits and customs. From a practically help-less animal species, he has advanced by the grace of whatever incentive lay behind his unique person-ality into a being endowed with a curious passion for improvement along many lines. By the sheer power of his mental processes, aided by the use of his fin-gers, a few crude but useful weapons and tools have been constructed, indicating great progress in his scale of living. The art of fishing in its simplest form, the employment of the snare for the capture of small game, and the pitfall as a means of trapping big animals have been developed. The list, at first glance, seems almost pathetic in its inadequacy, but if we stop a moment to realize the full significance of these accomplishments, what they mean to us at this late day, we shall be thrilled at the ingenuity and resourcefulness of those old-time artisans, and the mysterious forces which guided all their undertakings.

Man's peculiar and unique aspirations to raise himself above his surroundings, to acquire new skills superior to his earlier efforts, are responsible in large part for his remarkable accomplishments throughout all stages of his history. So many and so varied do these evidences of his growing ambition become that one is at a loss to even indicate more than a limited number of these most important events. As always, the need for food was paramount, increasingly so because of the constantly growing numbers of people to be found in the various camps and settlements throughout the human domain. Once started and firmly ensconced in his position as a governing force in the world of life, man proceeded, we may be sure, to oust all other animal species from the near vicinity of his meager habitations, and to be at continual odds with everything and everybody whose presence jeopardized in any way his feeling of security. The great destroyer was fast getting into his stride, even during those earlier years of his selfish and eventful career.

No longer were the sharpened stick and the jagged stone and the later rough bone or stone spear point fastened on a shaft sufficient for the needs of our ancestors as they slowly advanced into more specialized ways of living. The spear points became more neatly fashioned, the rough flints grew finer in form, more beautifully and cleverly made, and the hand axes, at first so crude and clumsy, now assumed useful and even graceful proportions. A quantity of varied tools—gravers, scrapers, borers, and eventually adzes and picks—were for the most part made from the highly important flint nodules, all broken, selected, and retouched by experts in the various communities scattered over widely separated parts of the continents of the eastern hemisphere.

The strange and significant fact that early man might have lived and even developed after a fashion *without* progressing to the use of tools and weapons becomes of great importance. Several species of big chimpanzee-like primates living contemporaneously and in fairly close proximity to ancient man, remained for ages in a relatively static condition mentally, and are still restricted to teeth and fingernails as weapons of offense and defense. Not so with our savage progenitors. Nothing they could possibly imagine was too difficult for them to adopt and improve upon either as a weapon or an implement for peaceful purposes. The once clumsy spear blossomed into a weapon of terrible efficiency; and the spear thrower, and later the bow and arrow, provided our hardy and tenacious relatives with a galaxy of life-destroying weapons with which he set out to annihilate everything in sight, human or otherwise. These wonderful productions of his clever hands would seem to have been sufficient for the needs of our august relatives, for with them they could kill big game and human enemies, and fight off attacks of predatory carnivora bent on mischief.

Animal food, however, comprised only a part of man's resources in things which would sustain life. There were fruits and nuts and berries at certain seasons; roots, tubers, bark, and branches and fagots for burning. All these were awkward and difficult items to carry for long distances, so that some kind of utensil, some means of transporting them, became almost a necessity in man's domestic economy. At first, the carrier might have been a huge leaf which held the plunder, but certainly it was not long before some clever brain had thought up the better scheme of plaiting or weaving the leaves roughly together. At this point it was but a step in evolution to the primitive basket shape which could be carried either on the head, close against the side, or dragged along the ground. The idea was an excellent one, so good, in fact, that after hundreds of thousands of years practically all the peoples of the world still use the basket in a more elaborate form.

It is quite possible that in ancient times the intro-

duction of this primitive bit of useful handiwork
assumed a new significance for prehistoric woman-
hood. With a strap or liana across her forehead, she
could attach and support on her back a basket filled
with heavy objects, pieces of dismembered game, fish,
and all the other edible objects so greatly preferred
by her lord and master. Or she could balance the
heavily loaded container on her head, walking upright and carefully to preserve the precious freight.
Perhaps, too, a baby could be carried in that way,
either on her head or across her back. The artificial,
handmade objects had therefore a variety of uses,
even if they were mostly of a rather homely order.
The men of the clan no doubt felt that their womenfolk could more easily do a hard day's work when
thus artificially assisted, while *they* could better spend
their time in hunting, fishing, exploring, and decimat-
ing their enemies.

All these various domestic activities were not, of
course, able to satisfy man's insatiable ambitions.
As time passed we see him engaged in many new and
sometimes far-reaching activities. Like children ever
seeking new worlds to conquer, the venturesome
spirit of ancient human beings caused them to em-
bark, literally, upon various local exploratory expeditions. A floating log was naturally the earliest of all
boats, but man soon improved upon this precarious
contrivance by felling tree trunks of his own choos-

ing. These, in later ages, he hollowed out by the use
of fire and by considerable chipping with a stone or
bone adze. The ends of the log were either left
square or bluntly pointed for greater ease in poling
about in shallow water. Rafts of wood or rushes also
served as means of transportation on the inland
waters. In these double aids to navigation we see the
first fruits of one of man's greatest future activities.
Fishing under such favorable circumstances flourished as never before, and with a well-sharpened
wooden spear or harpoon, a man could transfix the
prey with ease and celerity or trap the shining hordes
by means of simple nets.

Primitive Dugout Canoe

The housing problem must have been considered
of great importance in those far-off days, and the
very early leaf-covered structure was later abandoned
for something far more substantial and practical.
A sort of primitive hut was constructed when a number of upright sticks were set in a circle and covered
by a water-resisting thatch of dried grass or leaves.
The center of the hut was supported by a higher pole

than those used in the side walls, which provided a
sloping roof for the edifice and greatly facilitated
the shedding of rain water. The upright sides of the
hut were probably closed in by a series of interwoven
leaves or grasses, and a tiny hole at one side allowed
entrance. Not much of a home according to the
notions of civilized man, but one still used after
countless ages by great numbers of primitive peoples
the world over.

The boundless ego of the human animal is, and
apparently always has been, one of his chief characteristics. He was no doubt a show-off from his
primal inception, and that peculiar trait carried to
its logical conclusions can account for many of man's
special reactions to others of his own species and to
life in general. Presumably the profound emotions
of this strange being are not unique with man, because they are clearly linked with the sexual characters and practices of many types of living creatures.
Self-awareness, highly concentrated in many animal
types, is usually most evident during the breeding
periods when the desire to exhibit one's special
prowess or attractiveness is at its highest level of
emotional stress. The extraordinary displays made
by various bird species are truly wonderful confirma-
tions of this determination by the male to rivet attention upon his own special personality in order to
insure the acquiescence of the female bird in the

matter of procreation. It is not surprising, therefore, that man, who we must remember is a true mammal when it comes to his physical constitution, should under similar circumstances behave in the same manner as many of his lowlier relatives.

While he is also able to strut about in strange and ludicrous ways calculated to interest the onlooker, man's superability to decorate his person in outlandish fashion cannot be overlooked. The dandy is by no means confined to the later years of man's existence, but must have originated at a very early time. The long years of his upspringing have been brightened by countless successions of beads and bangles, nose rings, earrings, necklaces, anklets, and dozens of other varied gewgaws, all employed in the gentle art of decorating and thereby calling attention to his august person. These multifarious bits of manufactured or natural objects are still in constant use by untutored races and one need only stroll down the principal street of any city in America to have visual evidence of the fact that the ancient custom retains a large and special place even in our so-called advanced civilization.

The underlying reasons for the apparent slackening of interest in self-decoration among men in civilized communities are not easily explained. Even in early historic times the lure of the female of the species was increased by the use of extraneous aids to what was then considered mere natural beauty, but today, the tremendous force of business propaganda centers most of its energies in the field of clothing and ornament for the superdecoration of the weaker sex. This merely amplifies a trend in human nature developed in a remote period of human history, and perhaps prehistoric antiquity. Uncivilized man, however, still sees fit to decorate *his* person in some ornate manner, either rivaling or far exceeding in elaborateness anything exhibited by his consort.

In the course of this narrative we have repeated ourselves when speaking of the inception and material progress of our ancient stock. Weapons have been frequently mentioned, and several other simple cultures have been traced somewhat casually from very early times. This repetition is necessary because man's reactions to his various inventions resulted often in the adoption of other innovations more or less advanced in their construction, while he still retained the use of some earlier means of gaining a livelihood. And we must not forget that to the men of early days there were not many factors other than food and shelter which appeared necessary to their existence. Consequently the making of weapons and more weapons, together with domestic requisites of stone or bone, loomed large in their daily routine.

It is surprising how man, at first so simple and

frugal in his living requirements, came gradually to a point of almost extreme complication in the mere business of existing. He was a born elaborator, never content (at least after his earliest human stage) to remain in a state of comparative ease. We have seen him first as a mammal only, gathering his sustenance from the trees and bushes, then later as an awakened creature of a peculiarly ambitious disposition, eager, restless, and determined to proceed somewhere on the slightest provocation. A span of years beyond our conception passed before this youthful era was lived through, but the underlying spirit of our ancestors never faltered. Gradually, by means of their increasing ability to create and understand material things, they progressed to higher spheres of mentality.

Why man should have felt the need of so many varying approaches to his existence as a distinctly human animal is quite beyond our comprehension. If we could understand that colossal about-face from the old mammalian type, the great mystery of life might be one step nearer to solution. For it is a tremendously inspiring panorama that we have been considering, though still in its earlier stages. Our ancestors had something beneath those grimy and repellent exteriors, something to make us wonder about and to ponder over in our more thoughtful moments.

In later chapters, we shall learn about the actual

discoveries of man's somewhat sparse fossilized remains, the environment of each group, and guess at the climate and the customs of succeeding types of early man as he climbed from obscurity into the full light of his tremendous and far-reaching personality. The pageant, perhaps a million years in length, resolves itself in its final analysis into the simple fact that the being we call man had a mysterious and altogether unusual beginning, that in a period of time not long in the course of ancient world history, he was able to rise to his present exalted state, aided by objects created by his own skill and imagination. The first fruits of these profound cultural attributes have been roughly enumerated, but we shall see how greatly they have been elaborated in succeeding ages, though their basic excuses for being have changed only slightly during the same lengthy time period.

The spiritual factor also, while greatly altered in its external character, may not, after all, be so very different today from man's earlier conceptions of a possible life in the hereafter. The impact for thousands of years past of ideas promulgated by religious sects has not, in our opinion, greatly altered the deeper realms of man's thoughts and reflections; nor have their conflicting suggestions added greatly to our actual knowledge of the truth in the matter of man's ultimate state of being.

Man, on account of his dual nature and the extraordinary extent of his mental development, is a type
very difficult to understand. While we all appreciate
the truth of this statement when applied to ourselves,
we must realize that the perplexity of our ancestor's
trends and movements is of very long standing. Why
he did certain things when apparently there was no
reason for them is a problem both fascinating and
in many cases still unsolved.

Among these curiously difficult traits the desire to
migrate while living under what might seem agree-
able local conditions is a most peculiar phenomenon,
but the constant urge to move about is always apparent in man's history, even during its earlier stages.
He seems as a creature obsessed with strange yearnings, as though fettered in some sinister manner by
the difficulties attending his existence here. There
appears to be no reason for such emotions other than
the push and pull quality of his everlasting ego, a
beneficent agent for his material accomplishments,
but also a tragic force in binding his spirit when it
sometimes might reach a new plane of superior living. There can be no doubt that man has had to pay
a high price in mental depression and frustration
simply because of his ability to recognize and feel
these abstruse, and not easily subdued, emotions.
Such experiences, we can imagine, were not unknown

to our ancestors, especially as they continued to grow and develop mentally at an amazing rate.

Physically we have not changed so very greatly from our early days of the upright-standing attitude which had brought such marvelous results. However that may be, a survey of the known localities where fossil remains of man have come to light will reveal the truth of the statement that in him we have the traveler incarnate, even though he went places simply on his own two feet, with no knowledge of where he was bound or what he might find in food and general living conditions when he reached his destination. But such vague prospects never seem to have troubled our ancestors, who packed up their wives and children and a trusty spear or two and started off without any qualms for the wonderful unknown of their pre-historic dreams.

It is more than probable that all these things didn't happen for hundreds of thousands of years after our most primitive selves had crossed over from the apelike to the human status of being. Perhaps they, in those distant days, never thought anything about moving, except locally or under bad climatic conditions. We are told by the geological experts that vast changes in the land and water surfaces of the earth certainly did occur at intervals during man's sojourn here, but the story was an old one as far as our planet was concerned, since changing conditions—geologic and climatic—had been going on ever since the world was first created. Old Mother Nature, we fear, has not been sufficiently concerned about her children at these crucial times, because whole regions of the earth's crust, with all the life thereon, have been either obliterated or partially destroyed. Man naturally, as a part of a created universe, was exposed at all stages of his career to these same titanic forces and suffered accordingly, in some instances being cut off from his former continental habitat by a great catastrophe or an actual and practically permanent rise or fall of the sea level. This may have been the case in the life of the Java ape man, *Pithecanthropus,* whose earlier and more apelike ancestors are found fossilized in certain parts of India.

When we consider how relatively fragile are the bones of prehistoric man, and the presumable scarcity of the species in the living state, it is amazing that anything of the skeleton is left to bear witness to a former existence. Long before the time when man became sufficiently advanced mentally to feel the necessity of burying his dead, a huddled little heap of defunct humanity had sunk into the deep carpet of the forest floor or served to assuage the hunger of a passing hyena or other equally ravenous carnivora. The same applies as well not only to all species and races of early humans but also to modern man, wherever a contemporary type still remains in a primitive stage of culture. Under these precarious conditions, the actual unearthing of the bones of early man is classed as a red-letter incident in the fortunes of any modern anthropologist. Unfortunately such days are all too few, and the remains, even when carefully handled, are usually fragmentary, or at best very incomplete. Occasionally good luck does fall to the experts when some age-old treasure—a skull or a few leg and arm bones or merely an isolated tooth—emerges to gratify the gods of science in the person of a very tired but happy collector.

Had man always remained in the presumably congenial surroundings of his early era, his difficulties and dangers, formidable as they were, could have been surmounted with greater and greater ease as his mental growth taught him how to manufacture his early tools and weapons. But his restless ego urged him further and further afield so that eventually he found a haven, such as it was, in almost every corner of the eastern habitable globe. China, India and its islands, the Holy Land, and Europe were all occupied at times by our dirty, doughty ancestors who infiltrated like an invading army into pristine regions never before seen by man.

And what an extraordinary world it must have been, teeming with animal life of every sort which

was unafraid at first of the small two-legged creature in its midst, but soon learned by painful experience to regard him as an enemy. Here was no
fierce and quick moving saber-toothed tiger or
hungry wolf but a strange being who seemed able to
attack and kill them in many new ways. And so they
avoided him whenever possible, or fled wildly when
the peculiar telltale scent assailed their sensitive
nostrils. But against this new enemy, their well-
tried tactics for preservation too often failed.
Flaming pieces of wood flourished by grimy hands
frightened the herds of horses, antelopes, and deer
into precipitate retreat, and nets and pitfalls accounted for scores of casualties as the panicky animals dashed frantically about until they were slowly
encircled by their crafty human destroyers. The
hitherto fairly peaceful world of nature was to learn
the terrible menace of a new and sinister type of living creature, intelligent beyond all others and
equipped in new and dreadful ways to compete with
success in life's arena.

Undoubtedly man, wherever he went, carried his
culture with him—his weapons and tools and
baskets, but above all his own peculiar skills and
tenacious characteristics. As he traveled ever farther
westward on his pilgrimages, he encountered cooler
and more severe climatic conditions. Low temperatures necessitated clothing of some sort, not merely

for decoration but for the warmth that it imparted
to a shivering body. Animals slain in hunting were
skinned roughly and the raw hides dried and subsequently tanned in a primitive way by manipulation.
At any rate the wearing of some sort of extra covering must have been practically obligatory for the
warm country émigrés even though the long journey from their tropical environment had extended
over perhaps thousands of years. Blood heat must
be maintained at any cost, so that fire, warm furs,
and the best shelter possible were all necessities in
the more northern regions of man's increasingly
enlarged habitat.

Not only weather had to be accounted for, but
new species of wild animals must be confronted and
overcome, and this adventure entailed new hunting
methods and new weapons. Thus ages passed,
climates changed, cataclysms occurred, gigantic volcanic eruptions brought earthquakes, lava, and ashes
in such power and volume that whole regions were
engulfed and destroyed, yet our vigorous relatives
managed in some extraordinary way to maintain
themselves in moderately comfortable circumstances.
Sometimes they emerged, for a time at least, when
life was not too terribly strenuous, and again they
were retired into comparative oblivion by natural
forces of great severity and magnitude.

Strangely enough, life is so constituted that an

animal (including our own type) gradually becomes accustomed to almost incredibly difficult
situations, adapting its personality to strange, new,
and adverse conditions in a very miraculous way.
Nature is nothing if not tenacious, and the human
waif had received a very large and useful share of
that most necessary quality. As a rule, then, once
he had settled upon some special region in which to
live and bring up his family, it took a major change
of climate or a geological variation of great magnitude to dispossess him. Such climatic vicissitudes,
however, he was to encounter, especially in the better
known eras of his later history, when the great re-
curring Ice Ages swept across the land, greatly
lowering the normal temperatures in many parts of
the world and in Europe in particular. At such times,
the warm country fauna retreated to the southern
ranges of their habitat, their places being taken by
other species of animals better fitted to withstand
the cold.

The recurrent fluctuations in climatic conditions,
even though the period in question is restricted, are
far greater than would appear at first to a casual
observer. Weather variations occur day by day, and
life, to maintain itself with any sort of regularity,
must be kept in a high state of efficiency in order to
successfully maintain its normal level of growth and
perpetuation. Civilized man, although he rarely real-

A home site in the Mt. Carmel region of Palestine

A Neanderthal warrior

izes the fact, is being continually bolstered by favorable living surroundings for the same ultimate reason. We strive to keep ourselves warm in winter, cool in summer, well-fed and clothed, and generally looked after so that both the inner and the outer man shall feel himself refreshed and able to cope with what we call living conditions.

Even under favorable circumstances the delicate and precarious level of man's living regime must have always been a tremendous problem, constantly tending to fall to a danger line from which there could be no escape but death itself. Of all living things man apparently is the only one that has thus far been able, by dint of hard work and sagacity, to almost completely circumvent his environment and to secure eventually his own physical salvation whenever it was humanly possible. With the result that, whatever his numbers in the primitive stages (and they were probably few), each succeeding age has seen a vast increase in population, and today we are confronted with the astounding truth that there are by far too many people in the world and that, if for no other reason, the struggle for mere existence has become an ever-increasing menace to the continuance of the human species.

This sinister and very dangerous state of affairs has been constantly before our eyes in recent years, but there seems no way to alleviate the difficulty which has already assumed global proportions. In prehistoric times no such condition could have prevailed because vast reaches of untrodden areas of forest and plain stretched around the sparsely settled districts where man lived, and game of all kinds abounded. Flesh eaters naturally preyed upon the comparatively defenseless herbivora, but neither saber-toothed cats nor grisly hyenas made much impression upon their numbers.

Before the advent of man, nature seemed to have been able to balance in a general way the various primal conditions of life in the form of the vast assemblage of plants and animals which were to be found in all parts of the habitable globe. To be sure, after the passage of sufficient time and the consequent changes in environment, complete annihilation of countless individuals, species, and orders of living forms had occurred. But the process was an infinitely slow one, comprising whole eras in its accomplishment.

While all this may have been generally true for those gigantic time periods which had preceded our ancestor's appearance, the state of world affairs *after* that fateful event was to assume a very different aspect. For with the introduction of man's personality, insignificant as it may have appeared in its infancy, some new and exceedingly virile potential was to gradually assume at least a partial control over the vital balance of natural things and forces. This was indeed a revolutionary condition, something unique in global experience, but the story of the rise of man from the apelike beings of his earlier environment will amply prove the truth of the statement. We must not forget one very important point —the vastly accelerated speed of man's domination of nature in the very latest period of his development as compared with the long, slow processes of physical and cultural advancement which preceded that extraordinary denouement.

Time estimates of man's existence on this planet vary so tremendously according to different authorities that it is quite impossible to do more than average them for our own better comprehension of the subject. Let us assume that a million years have passed since our monkeylike relatives scampered about in perhaps either Africa or Asia, each intent upon his own little business of living. From that time on he has never ceased to exist as a creature, nor has he ever relinquished his hold on the helm of his ship of state, even though at first that ship was only a log of wood floating in a primeval swamp. We have only faintly suggested in our text how far he has come from that insignificant beginning, but we must admit (and the thought can really give us satisfaction) that he has advanced mightily, especially within the last 100,000 years or so of his existence. By this time he seems to have thrown off many of his more primitive characteristics although, particularly in his physical appearance, he was still not quite a human being.

Perhaps 50,000 years have come and gone since the first actually manlike creatures made their appearance in western Asia and Europe. But their ancestors, coming as we think they did from the east, may have been made in man's likeness for a much longer period. At any rate, we know his skeleton and much of his actual work from that time, and he seems to have been thoroughly equipped for the coming periods which were to extend his activities so vastly in every direction. Like a runner poised for a race, this ancient athlete had been severely trained for the career which he was to pursue right down to this very day. Because the phenomenon of the rise of man does not become very apparent until the 50,000-year period in his past, we must not assume anything sudden in his development. For he, like all other animated beings, was a built-up type of construction, mentally and physically. In any recapitulation of what happened to this strange primate to assure him first place in life's category of created things, great stress must be placed on the over-balancing weight of his intellectual proclivities. All in all, in spite of the short time that he has existed on our planet, he has done wonderful things, pushed aside many of nature's restrictions, developed his schemes of culture, and now finds himself confronted by a Pandora's box of possibilities which, if rightly comprehended, may still be able to lead him to the heights of his supreme destiny.

However this may be, and the facts which we glean from a study of man in the past would seem to bear out the assertion, there is quite another side to man's character, something of a much more prosaic nature which nevertheless has been of inestimable value to the modern scientist who seeks to unravel the mysteries of our early development. This primitive trait, which we call curiosity, is certainly not possessed exclusively by man, but as usual he has vastly elaborated upon its potentialities as seen in his simian relatives. Digging in the earth for food was naturally an early ancestral habit and one indulged in even at the present day by uncivilized men in many parts of the world, but the desire to upturn something hidden, some object as yet unseen, a treasure in fact, can also be associated with our long-defunct progenitors. Like all deeply seated emotions, this one seems to be inherent in man's very being. We still love to dig for hidden treasure, to pick up any strange object we may encounter, and to read in these finds an explanation of their origin and composition compatible with our knowledge of the subject.

Reference has been made to the many classical

allusions on the discovery and the possible significance of shells and bones of creatures long since passed away, and with what interest they were regarded by many of our forbears. Among such finds, the bones of man were almost never mentioned, either because of their scarcity or more probably because of a lack of interest on the part of the excavator. It may truthfully be said that for countless ages, even until a couple of hundred years ago, the principal reason for this groping about in strange places, turning over rocks, exploring caves, and bringing home various relics in the shape of more or less fragmentary remains of animal skeletons, curious stones, bits of pottery and other objects was merely man's eternal habit of acquisition. In this way he could possess something that the other fellow didn't have, thus imparting a kind of mysterious aura to his own person, and moreover the curiosities became a subject of speculation and wonder to his fellow clansmen. There is extant a vast and engrossing literature upon this ancient theme revealing, as a rule, a complete and sublime ignorance on the part of early writers.

We have already mentioned the very casual attention bestowed upon the earlier discoveries of the bones of prehistoric man up to about a hundred years ago. It would seem that at that late date such a remarkable incident would have caused a scientific

furor of no small proportion. It is not difficult, of
course, to moralize now on what might have happened, but it does seem strange, nevertheless, that
until quite recently the study of and the interest in
prehistoric man should have been a matter of so
little moment. No doubt the scarcity of working
material had much to do with this apparent professional apathy. In any case, such indifference is
now a thing of the past, and the learned gentlemen
who make the study of man a life occupation are
only too anxious to hear of or examine any scrap of
evidence tending to further enlighten them on this
fascinating line of investigation. Thus they hope
against hope that certain difficulties and discrepancies
in their always meager data will be clarified and decided upon by the new discoveries in excavations now
going on in various parts of the world.

It is interesting to observe that the practically new
science of prehistoric anthropology rather resembles
the proverbial snowball which gathers both impetus
and bulk as it proceeds on its way. Each new bit of
evidence is seized upon avidly and gone over meticu-
lously by carefully trained specialists who measure
every bump and hollow upon the skull of some early
extinct relative. Each cusp upon a partially complete
set of well-worn teeth is examined to determine
whether the owner was a monkey or a man.

For us, the extreme importance of such procedure

is interesting only as it indicates that a new and most complete survey is under way regarding our very selves in the days of our extremely early development. We are slowly learning what we were like in those far-off days from a close examination of all the skulls and pieces of the bony skeletons now being brought to light in various areas of the globe. What man *did,* aided by the advantage gained in the acquisition of the upright stance, his superior mental power, and manufactured tools and weapons, we must infer from a very intensive study of all the facts pertaining to his living habits. His many wonderful discoveries and inventions, even in his earlier career—basket making, pottery molding, boats and houses, and the discovery of the uses of fire—all these contributed tremendously in his rise to world pre-eminence. From the visual evidences of his slowly growing belief in a future for himself and his kindred, we see demonstrated the possibilities of his spiritual advancement which become more and more evident as time goes on. All in all, we are a composite piece of mechanism—physical, mental, spiritual, linked cleverly together—unpredictable, unstable, gloriously gifted but unable as yet to quite grasp the meaning of our own existence.

It will be, therefore, a highly congenial task to chronicle what evidence we have thus far amassed about this extraordinary creature, showing him at first as an apelike being whose existence must have closely approximated that of the high primates by which he was surrounded. Later we shall see how, as a distinctly sagacious type, he was able to manufacture for his own use many kinds of tools and weapons made from materials of his own choosing— wood and stone and bone, at first and later the metals, bronze and iron. All these things are highly suggestive, and together with the skeletal remains they comprise at least a part of what we really know about prehistoric man. But to learn more about him, pictures and drawings must be made to show as accurately as possible the forms and proportions of whatever skeletal remains we possess of the various types and species that have been discovered during the last hundred years. Accompanying these, detailed studies of some of his early and later weapons and tools will explain better than any written description the kind of things by which our ancestors were able to forge ahead in an environment too often beset with difficulties of no mean order.

EARLY TOOLS AND WEAPONS

Flint—an impure form of quartz, a silica hydrate —seems, interestingly enough, to have been regarded with the greatest appreciation by early man. The technique required for the proper working of this unique substance, harder but more brittle than steel, was one of man's earliest achievements in manual dexterity. At first, in fact, he merely collected suitable but naturally formed bits of the smooth, fine-grained stone and employed them in various crude and clumsy ways to help him in his difficult fight against extermination. The tremendous value of flint in the lives of ancient peoples can only be appreciated with difficulty by modern man whose immensely varied and efficient living accessories are almost without number. We can hardly picture ourselves in a situation where, for the want of a crude stone implement, our very lives would be endangered. Yet such would have been the case on many occasions in early days when the specter of starvation, or death from the attacks of some great animal, was often a reality, and a man unarmed or without some digging, cutting, or striking tool presented only a feeble and ineffectual front in such an emergency. So it was that our progenitors, at a very early date, cast about them for some stony material with which to augment the

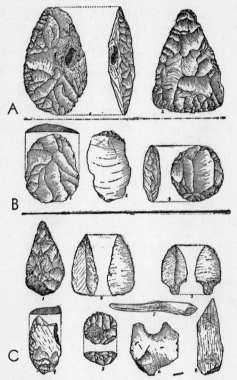

Courtesy American Museum of Natural History

Core Implements

Pieces of obsidian, flint or other stone from which flakes have been struck A: Typical Acheulian implements B: Typical Levalloisian implements C: Typical Mousterian implements

power of their none too powerful hands and feet and teeth in the battle against nature's unrelenting forces. With what satisfaction, then, our relative seized upon the very thing which was to help him out of his difficulties. For thus reinforced, his long arms could deal terrible blows, and when he had learned to break the stones the sharp edges of the shattered mass might gash and cut an adversary in a truly effective manner. Thus strengthened he also felt new courage in the face of an enemy no matter how formidable; and being what he was, a creature of superior mentality, he quickly recognized the possibilities of the newly discovered material. Subsequently, in the long ages of his development he learned to fashion and shape this valuable stone in a thousand ingenious ways, and all sorts of utensils, weapons, and ornaments were produced through succeeding generations of industry.

It is evident that the peculiar properties of the strange stone appealed not only to men living in a European environment, for it has been found fashioned artificially in many different countries. This almost universal employment is a further proof of the similarity of man's mental and physical economy and ambitions even when widely separated from others of his own species. We are not able to date with any accuracy the realization by our ancient relatives of the extreme value of the hard shiny

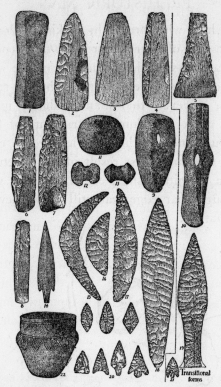

Typical Middle and Late Neolithic Implements

1. Grindstone	15. Flint sickle blade
2-5. Flint axes	16. Flint knife or saw
6. Flint adze	17. Flint saw
7. Flint gouge	18. Flint spearpoint or dagger
8. Flint chisel	19. Flint dagger
9. Stone axe-hammer	20. Flint arrow points (seven
10. Stone war axe	basic forms)
11. Stone club head	21. Flint arrow point
12-13. Amber beads or pendants	22. Pottery vessel, stamped or-
14. Slate spearpoint	namentation filled with chalk

nodules which, when broken by striking with another fragment, gave off sparks; nor how *that* phenomenon which made possible the production of fire was also to prove of incalculable value to the human race. We do know, however, that man gradually improved upon the crude and clumsy instruments of his first manufacture and that he later learned to chip the edges of the rough first result of the fracture and created a definitely sharp-edged tool or weapon, even though that edge was still very uneven and wavy in outline.

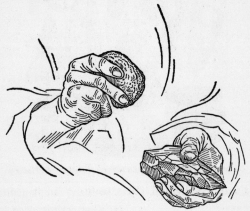

Method of Striking Flint

The men of those early days made constant use of these rough and awkward utensils, employing the heavy objects in digging, striking, cutting off pieces of flesh from the carcass of a dead animal, or crack-

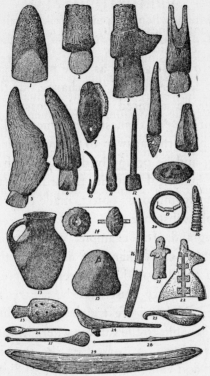

Typical Neolithic (Robenhausian) Implements

1-2. Stone axes
3. Jadeite axe (second form)
4. Stone axe (third form)
5. Stone axe (last form)
6. Jadeite chisel
7. Flint knife, set in wooden hand-
   hold
8. Flint knife, set in antler handle
9. Bone chisel or spatula
10. Fishhook made from boar's tooth
11. Split mammal bone awl
12. Bone awl, set in bone handle
13. Pottery vessel in form of pitcher
14. Burnt clay spindlewhorl
15. Burnt clay loom weight

16. Comb or bifurcated rib, for pressing
    down woof
17. Bone button, extra large
18. Antler pendant
19. Stone beads, cylindrical
20. Lignite bracelet. France
21. Burnt clay human figurine. France
22. Burnt clay ornamental idol.
    Austria
23. Wooden mallet
24. Axe showing details of hafting
25. Wooden dipper
26. Wooden ladle
27. Wooden club
28. Yew wood bow
29. Wooden boat or canoe

ing the long bones for the rich and toothsome marrow they contained. The simple life of early man was to grow less simple as time passed, and one of the great accelerators of this change was the decided advantage he acquired when he possessed a stone weapon or a useful domestic implement. Flint seemed to have been the answer to many problems of his existence, and he promptly directed much of his intellect and physical dexterity toward the manufacture of constantly improved objects made from the highly serviceable substance.

In England, for example, actual mines occur, places where early man dug deep into the clay in search of the flint nodules concealed there. A really important industry must have been carried on here for a long time and great quantities of the valuable material brought to the surface where it was bartered for other things, or worked on the spot into many preferred and valuable objects. Not all flint was thus procured because much of it, in already broken or shattered pieces, could be picked up by men who apparently spent a great deal of time in searching for them. Our early relatives, it must be remembered, had plenty of time on their hands. There was no daily rush to earn one's living, no night gaieties, no trips to distant places, and no rent bills at the end of the month. Food and its procuring, fights with neighbors, an occasional midnight foray in the hope

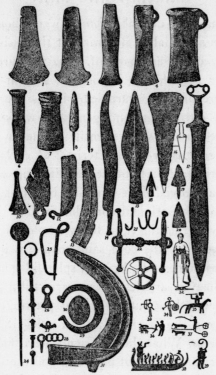

Courtesy American Museum of Natural History

Typical Implements of Bronze Age

1-5. Axe blades
6. Chisel
7. Hammer
8. Awl
9. Needle
10. Tweezers
11-12. Razors
13. Saw, fragmentary
14. Knife
15. Spear point
16. Dagger blade
17. Sword, double-edged
18-20. Arrow points
21. Fishhooks
22. Bit for horse bridle
23. Wheel for votive chariot, or possibly a pendant
24. Hairpins (6)
25. Fibula (safety pin)
26. Pendant, or part of a pendant
27. Bar-shaped button
28. Chain attached to pin
29. Bracelet
30. Sword hilt button
31. Sickle blade
32. Female figure with necklace, spiral arm rings, belt buckle, and dagger
33. Warrior with bow, arrow, and sword
34. Warrior with axe and shield
35. Warrior on horseback with spear and shield
36. Plowing with oxen
37. Horse-drawn chariot
38. Double-prowed vessel with warriors
39. Warrior blowing trumpet

of stealing some desirable female were about all the excitements available. But without the assistance of his flint accessories, many of these pleasures would have been curtailed or impossible, so that we have the picture of these sturdy aborigines everlastingly chipping, retouching, and generally working upon their much-prized stone utensils whenever possible.

One very marked characteristic of early production was the fact that at first very little use was made of the sharp-edged chips struck off by blows upon the surfaces of the original core, but in later ages the reverse was true, the chips being employed in countless ways, while the core sank to a less important level of usefulness. To be sure, splendid spear points and the heavier articles in use were still made from the central nucleus, but the cutting, piercing, scraping shapes were almost entirely the results of the chipping process. What these ancients were finally able to produce in the way of beautiful and useful objects in flint and other stones can only be judged by a glance at the plates here shown, and it is certain that a great amount of technical skill was required to turn out such symmetrical, graceful, and at the same time well-designed objects for daily use. The technique of flint chipping, curiously enough, is still not a lost skill, and the so-called "flint-knappers" in certain parts of England are able with much practice to turn out very creditable specimens of the flintworker's

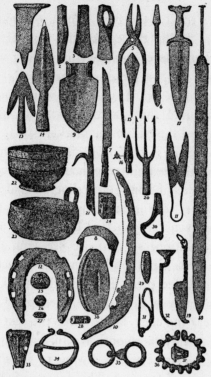

Courtesy American Museum of Natural History

Typical Implements of the Later Iron Age

1. Anvil
2. Hammer
3-4. Axes
5. Tongs
6. Auger
7. Combination knife-saw
8. Spokeshave
9. Plowshare
10. Scythe blade
11. Shears
12. Horseshoe
13. Harpoon point

14. Spear point
15. Iron arrow point
16. Bronze arrow point
17. Dagger
18. Double edged sword
19. Razor or knife
20. Fish spear
21. Boathook
22. Wood cup
23. Bronze cup
24. Bone dice
25-28. Polychrome mosaic glass beads

29. Amber pendant
30. Bronze safety pin
31. Iron safety pin
32. Bronze hairpin
33. Bronze brooch
34. Bronze buckle
35. Iron belt hook and ring
36. Bronze bracelet
37. Gold finger ring
38. Strike-a-light stone

art. Commercially, the field is now of course very limited, but during the era of the flintlock musket, many workers were employed in various countries to turn out by the hundreds the small, specially shaped bits of the hard substance, which under concussion produced the spark necessary to ignite the powder behind the ball in the musket barrel.

By what process our progenitors discovered the fact that by pressure either with another piece of flint or a hard piece of bone small slivers could be pried off the original core is naturally a mystery, but mysteries to man merely whetted his appetite for their successful solution, so that we see him gradually acquiring an uncanny ability in that direction. By holding the large piece firmly in the hand, and by pushing strongly with a dull-pointed piece of bone or stone near the edge, but towards the center of the main core, a curious smooth fracture was produced, a form of cleavage which, owing to its shape, we call a *conchoidal fracture*. This fracture is also produced by striking a hard blow upon any so-called platform or flattened surface of the flint. This almost unique property, and the clever way in which he took advantage of it were two things of epoch-making value to early man. Living as he did in the midst of dangers and privation, it was of incalculable value to possess this wonderful adjunct in his scheme of living. A flint tool, because of this peculiar type of cleavage, was easily resharpened or reshaped, the spearheads fined down again for use against any adversary, and scrapers and hand axes given a new lease on life by a little expert manipulation.

Method of Flaking Flint by Pressure

If, as has been said, the earlier forms of flint utensils were concerned only with the use of the resultant core after the chips had been removed, the later fashion rather reversed this sequence, and the chips themselves were employed in many important ways. Indeed, so characteristic are the forms and methods of chipping during successive ages, that many anthropologists regard them as most useful objects for dating a particular place and period, and a vast amount of literature has resulted from long and continuous study of their various shapes, the techniques employed in making them, and the uses to which they have been put by their original producers. Still later in human prehistory and before the discovery of the metallic substances, bronze and iron, man continued his manufacture of flint utensils, but instead of leaving them in a rough, even though delicately retouched condition, some of the surfaces at least were polished by the application of sand and water as an abrasive. At first only the cutting edges of the various tools were thus treated, but eventually the entire surface of the objects in question, hatchets, hammerstones or knives, etc., were completely and beautifully finished in the new technique. This type of culture was actually to name a certain great period of man's history: the Neolithic (new) or Polished Stone Age, thus indicating to the anthropologist a difference between this period and the previous one, viz. the Paleolithic, or Old Stone Age, when polishing of implements was not the general rule. In fact, the use of flint, and the varying techniques employed in its preparation, are so much part and parcel of our history and development that the two stories go hand in hand in any recapitulation of our earlier culture, because early life itself would have been well-nigh impossible without it during the thousands of years of man's primitive and strenuous existence.

Naturally, other types of rock, as well as bone, ivory, and wood were employed in the important utensil manufacture in many parts of the primitive world. Obsidian, a natural volcanic glass, is an excellent substitute where sharpness of point and edge is the principal objective, but the highly brittle material could hardly be employed where weight, toughness, and great solidity were essential. In the making of fire, no other substance apparently could supplant flint as a spark producer. The incandescent particles struck off by a powerful blow were intensely hot, and therefore easily controlled by a skilled hand as they fell flaming upon a dried surface of some easily ignitable substance, preferably moss or wood dust. Man's best friend in his earlier days was not a living canine, but a hard, cold chunk of impure quartz.

The phenomenon of man as a living creature, and his place and progress in a world of animal life, have now been traced in a general way, as well as man's own interest in himself as a being possessing unique physical, mental, and moral qualities. This survey, though reviewed in a few pages, has dealt with a subject of immense and extraordinary import to all sensitive and speculative people. No one of us can afford to be unacquainted with the fundamental facts concerning our own early origin, nor the implication of those facts when applied to the present problems of our earthly residence. This knowledge, while it will not solve the difficulties by which we are confronted, can nevertheless help to explain in some measure the peculiar traits of the human animal and his special reactions under the

stress and strain of conflicting ideologies now so
evident in world economy. It may also bring realization of the truth that the average individual is not
and never has been a creature of very high moral
standards and that, with the exception of certain
deeply religious or highly cultured and well-trained
individuals, we can not expect too much in the way
of truly superior aspirations in the direction of a
more altruistic viewpoint on affairs of the very greatest significance to our general welfare. Especially
are these matters difficult to accomplish in a world
which is overpopulated to the danger point and therefore affords a minimum of assurance for any form
of peace and security.

A little serious thought upon this engrossing subject will reveal the truth of the above statement, but
it will not preclude the assumption of a very realistic
conception of our present plight, nor the determination to so adapt ourselves to circumstances that we
may gradually find a way out of our difficulties. The
number of human beings now living upon our planet
has assumed such fantastic proportions that we can
hardly realize the paucity in figures of our ancient
parent stocks, nor how little they counted in a teeming mammalian world. In our time, these widely
scattered nuclei of the human species have so tremendously multiplied that, like ants upon their
dwelling hill, we must be prepared to organize our-

selves with the utmost intelligence and wisdom and be willing to submit to certain disciplinary measures for the conservation of all our various assets and activities.

Exactly the reverse of these conditions must have assailed our primitive ancestors, whose domain lay in the great open spaces of a hard, inhospitable world, where everything but man himself existed in vast numbers; great and dangerous beasts of various kinds, and unknown forces too terrible to contemplate combined to present a picture of fearful isolation to our cringing and ever-alert relatives. If we may judge from the scarcity of their remains thus far unearthed, these lowly creatures existed in small groups, perhaps on the edge of some great forest area into whose protecting depths they could plunge when danger threatened. At present our knowledge of the little fellows is intriguing and significant, but painfully meager in numbers of individuals and partially complete skeletons. South Africa seemed to have been a congenial homesite for this small section of the early human family, but later discoveries may immeasurably extend this range into regions as yet undiscovered.

A short résumé of the field of prehistory may not be amiss here, in order to clarify our ideas of what has been accomplished during the last hundred years of truly scientific and enlightened research upon the subject. While we shall later attempt to relate the history and significance of the various very important finds up to the present time, they will not be arranged in chronological sequence, but rather upon their anatomical progression from the lowest known forms up to the advent of truly manlike types. It is of interest, however, to take first the actual finds in their true sequence, because these discoveries reacted upon one another in a rather confusing way, and gave rise to many speculations and differences of opinion regarding man's development through long ages of his history.

As we now look back upon these often acrimonious differences of opinion, there is evident a gradual change of ideas as to our actual derivation from possible very lowly varieties of humanity. Conclusions of which we have already spoken and which today are distinctly commonplace were not so long ago looked upon with actual horror and repugnance by gentle and well-educated peoples the world over. When, for example, about one hundred years ago the first Neanderthal skulls were found, the earliest at Gibraltar, and later the type from the Neander Valley in Germany, the creature seemed so unbelievably primitive that even most of those learned men who accepted its authenticity were not able to conceive of anything much lower in the human scale. When, a few years later, the now well-known skeletons of the splendid Cro-Magnon race came to light in France and England, the issue was again doubly confused, for these great fellows were evidently actual human beings like ourselves—tall, intelligent, and well formed in every way.

Again in 1892 the scientific world received a new shock when Professor Eugene Dubois, a Dutch scientist, discovered in Java the skullcap, femur and a tooth or two of the so-called *Pithecanthropus,* which he was positive possessed the characteristics of an extremely early manlike animal. The creature was very much older than Neanderthal man, more monkeylike in every way (almost a missing link) and therefore a most objectionable object in the eyes of the fundamentalist die-hards for years after its stormy advent. Once more the scientific world grew big-eyed as they contemplated this extremely lowly progenitor. But in 1907, a fine lower jaw with perfect teeth and in a splendid state of preservation was exposed in a deep gravel pit of the Mauer Sands near Heidelberg in Germany. This huge jaw was apparently intermediate in development between the Neanderthal and the *Pithecanthropus* races of manlike creatures, and served as a premise for discussion among all classes and professions because of its massive quality and the distinct impression of brutish strength which it conveyed. Later, in 1912, a fragmentary skull of a new subhuman species came to

light in Piltdown-Sussex, England. Now known as
the Piltdown skull, it again caused widespread discussion in professional circles.

The European field being apparently exhausted
for the time being, our survey takes us far across
the world to China, where at Chu-Ku-Tien, not
far from Peking, Dr. Davidson Black, a Canadian
scientist, described a new variety of humans which
he named *Sinanthropus,* the Chinese man. The conditions and results of this truly remarkable piece of
research will later be described in more detail. Here
we shall place the creature somewhere between the
Neanderthal and *Pithecanthropus* types, immensely
ancient, primitive, and altogether wonderful.

We shift again in this casual survey to the Holy
Land not far from Jerusalem to the great caves in
the side of a rocky hill where in 1924, Miss Dorothy
Garrod and Dr. McCown excavated a whole series
of remarkable skeletons which as yet, owing to various difficulties, are not very well known to us. They
are seemingly a mixture, as far as our information goes, of two great families of early man—the
Neanderthal and Cro-Magnon species.

Back to China again in looking over what we know
of ancient man's dwelling places; South China this
time and a most intriguing and romantic story of
a possible giant race of humans, *Gigantopithecus,* the
result of a lucky discovery in a Chinese apothecary

shop in Hong Kong by Dr. Von Koenigswald, a young Dutch scientist who also at about the same time discovered more and most valuable remains of the old *Pithecanthropus* in Java.

Another big jump and we are in South African wilds where, in 1924, Dr. Raymond Dart came upon the last, or rather the first word in human development—*Australopithecus*—a child's skull of such apelike character that only an expert could separate the infant from that of a chimpanzee baby. This was the most primitive human animal thus far described. A little later, in 1936, Dr. Robert Broom, also in South Africa, blasted from the hard and difficult matrix several almost apelike skulls, but with certain things about them decidedly leaning toward the human side of development. These little fellows were indeed a revelation and a tremendously important link in our chain of evidence regarding the form of man's extremely early progenitors.

Thus, it has taken the scientific world about a hundred years from the first really serious studies of the subject to discover what appears to be a creature that might indeed be the celebrated and much discussed "missing link," which heretofore had been a mere word applied to a fanciful creature. If in succeeding chapters man's life story is not always a perfect one in its orderly development, we are fortunate in having found even such scanty evidence as

we now possess to aid in filling the gaps in a history
so engrossing but so vague and dimly indicated in
many of its earlier episodes. The wonder is that, in
spite of the extreme scarcity of actual skeletal remains and their fragmentary condition when discovered, as well as the huge areas over which the
material is distributed, collectors have been clever
enough to uncover many highly important bits of
information for the translation of an exciting chapter
in nature's book of life.

At any rate, the patient men of science, working at
times under very difficult circumstances, have finally
amassed a sufficient amount of skeletal material to
piece together the long story of our ancestral progress and evolution through the ages of human
history. The romance is an extraordinary one,
unique among all others, but it is naturally still far
from complete. Undoubtedly in the years to come
there will be new finds of equal or even greater
significance. Certain blind spots in our present state
of information will be clarified, perhaps in a very
surprising way, and the Americas, North and South,
may yet disclose new species or forms much earlier
and more primitive than any yet discovered on the
two vast continents. At present, however, all finds of
early man in America have been classified, under
expert analysis, as merely older forms of the American Indian. Should any really early types eventually

be unearthed, it might cause a readjustment of the whole line of primitive humanity right down through the ages.

It has been well said that a study of the past will reveal many facts of value in our own time, but it will also help us to visualize the future in a progressive, concrete manner. These statements are doubly true in the case of man because only by a knowledge of what we once were can we understand our present position, and what we may become in a swiftly changing world environment. In that future time, even more than in the present era, we shall need as never before every stalwart and courageous trait in man's inner character in order to maintain ourselves against the powers of evil in whatever guise they may appear.

The story we are about to tell will reveal, as nothing else can, that fundamentally man's inner spirit, his soul, his ego, call it what you will, must have been latent in his physical and mental constitution from the time of his first appearance as an incipient but unusual form of created being. There is no dogma attached to this statement, but with all due deference to the opinions of the biologists, the chemists, and the dyed-in-the-wool realists in all scientific lines, it seems to the writer that unless some such attribute be accepted as a fact, there is no other way of explaining man's story, his actions, his accomplishments, and his extraordinary divergences from every other type of mammal both past and present. No predictions as to his ultimate future are here presented, but the salient traits apparent in his cosmos are related as they have been revealed to us by a study of all the material at present in our possession.

ACTUAL HISTORY OF FINDS

In the preceding pages in the order of their discovery we have given the approximate dates and places where such finds occurred. The following pages tell the same story except that it is much more complete and shows in the successive stages man's physical and mental growth from the primitive to the modern. While humanity in general is inclined to refute, or does not care to admit, close relationship with the higher apes, there is always a kind of childlike eagerness present in some of us to picture and be thrilled by the possibility of such a contingency.

How often have we heard during the years the term "missing link" applied to any new find of the remains of prehistoric man, no matter how recent these relics may really be. Scientists are always scornful of the term because it has a suspiciously amateur sound and is used so frequently by circus barkers and

Danger under the moon

Wild cattle driven to the edge of a precipice

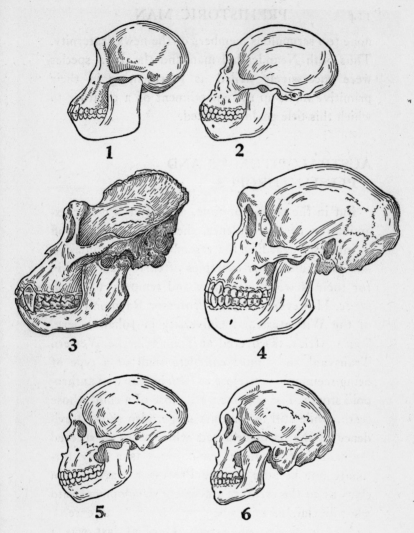

Comparative Study of Skulls

(drawn to the same scale—⅙ natural size)

1. Plesianthropus, 2. Pithecanthropus, 3. Modern gorilla, 4. Gigantopithecus, 5. Neanderthal, 6. Cro-Magnon

none too scrupulous members of the news fraternity. Thus both Neanderthal man and the Java species were successively hailed as representing in their primitive make-up the embodiment of a creature to which this title could be affixed.

AUSTRALOPITHECUS AND PLESIANTHROPUS

But in the course of time, and after a closer examination of the evidence, there was a falling off in interest regarding the resemblance to a monkey-like form, and other examples of early man came in for their share of notoriety and temporary prominence. However, in 1924, Professor Raymond Dart of the Witwatersrand University in Johannesberg, South Africa, discovered at Taungs in the Western Transvaal, the almost complete skull of a type of being seemingly very close to *both* human and anthropoid stocks. The remains were those of a child whose teeth, while still in the milk stage, also showed evidence of the permanent sets which were to succeed them. This transitional condition was a very fortunate one because it gave Professor Dart certain clues as to the creature's ultimate development into what he claimed might be a new form of an exceedingly primitive manlike type. Here at last was a veritable "missing link" for which we had been so long searching, and later study of the skull and face structures confirmed the original conjecture.

The professor of anatomy had finally proved, at least to the scientific world, that man and ape were at one time closely related, one to the other. It was, in fact, a complete justification of the inferential method of anatomical deduction, but it had taken almost a hundred years to demonstrate the value of such a proceeding. Naturally, there was skepticism and opposition in certain professional circles, but noted experts such as the Englishmen, W. J. Sollas and Sir Grafton Elliot-Smith, as well as Dr. William K. Gregory in the United States, and Dr. Robert Broom in South Africa, accepted the idea from the first and the *Australopithecus Africanus* is now ensconced among the first of our progenitors.

Technically, the brain capacity as indicated by the size of the skull would seem to be about that of a gorilla or chimpanzee, but the teeth, the facial angle, and other features lean a bit more towards the human side, so that all in all we are looking at a type of being which at least gives us an inkling of our own very ancient ancestors, even though this particular species may not be the archetype in our direct line of descent. No longer need we dream about our probable first appearance as we stepped across the narrow chasm which separated man from his anthropoid relatives, because that dream has now become a reality, rather prosaic to be sure, but intensely informative as it discloses to the expert eye an age-old difference, however slight, between ourselves and a much less progressive mammal of an almost similar physical appearance.

All these facts and a host of others concerning this so early waif of our possible parent lineage quite naturally fired Dr. Robert Broom's zeal as a collector. Like Dr. Dart, Broom had been formulating for a long time a theory that the continent of Africa might prove to be the home of excessively early human types. Both these gentlemen had encountered difficulties in putting through their ideas in this connection because of strong opposition from scientists who were wedded to the idea of an Asiatic origin for our ancestral stock. A considerable amount of discussion had been forthcoming upon this crucial bit of anthropological lore, and even now there are those among the fraternity who are still not convinced, though they claim to be open to conviction. In his day Charles Darwin had apparently rather embraced the African, as opposed to the Asiatic, home of early man, but as no actual data on the subject was available at the time, there was really nothing concrete behind his speculations. So great, however, was the knowledge accumulated by this Nineteenth Century genius that inference of any sort on his part was the result of a tremendous amount

of hard and splendidly trained thinking, and co-
ordinated reasoning of the highest order.

To Dr. Broom's well-trained eye there was something about this infantile antecedent that prompted
further search in the general vicinity of Taungs in
the hope that he might possibly unearth an adult of
the same or a similar species, a specimen better
developed in general characteristics than Dr. Dart's
child. With all the persistence and knowledge of
geological conditions for which Broom is famous, he
plodded away at his arduous task until finally in 1936
at a place called Sterkfontein, near Krugersdorp in
the Transvaal, he came across the incomplete adult
skull of a being not unlike the Taungs child, but
fortunately in a more highly developed physical
condition. This discovery could only further urge
Dr. Broom to continue his hunt for this most interesting creature, and he has now (in 1948) been
able to accumulate several not quite complete skulls
of the old type which he calls *Plesianthropus trans-
vaalensis*.

Only recently a pelvis, said on good authority to
be of a distinctly human and not apelike construction,
has also come to light in the very near vicinity of
the skull finds. This important part of the bony
anatomy poses a crucial question which is not easily
answered. If the pelvis had been actually *associated*
with the skull, it might have settled the extremely

vital question of the creature's ability to stand and walk in an upright manlike fashion. As we know, no great ape, owing to anatomical peculiarities, can quite accomplish this method of progression.

To the scientist such seemingly trivial differences are of prime importance in any discoveries involving very early manlike creatures, since he can detect in these differences certain trends of physical construction which, in their final analysis, may lead to decisions otherwise impossible to formulate. By this drastic but necessary method of procedure, the keen and resourceful investigator weighs all the evidence for and against any opinion as to the type of primitive being from which the races of men might have descended.

In the case of the pelvis, however, no conclusion has as yet been reached because the material in which the specimens were found is not stratified, as is often the case, but consists of what is known as *breccia,* a hard, stony matrix of broken rock fragments naturally cemented into a hard, refractory mass of conglomerate. Such an environment makes all collecting a very arduous and complicated task, and as in this instance increases the danger of misinterpretation to a considerable degree. In the history of the search for fossil remains, one often comes upon such an impasse, but the true scientist is not the man to slur over any such difficulty. Rather it stimulates him to greater effort, and he consults colleagues whom he knows to be specialists along certain lines, gives them all the data and listens carefully to their staid and well-thought-out opinions upon the subject in question.

As it stands, *Plesianthropus* is actually known only by his head and perhaps a few scattered bones. The manlike pelvis may or may not belong to him at all, in which case he is, for the present at least, condemned to assume a temporary quadrupedal attitude when walking or running. We hope that this condition is only temporary and that science will sooner or later admit that recalcitrant pelvis as part and parcel of this primitive creature, so that we can start man off on his long journey towards the strictly human type in his well-known upright standing and walking pose. There is, however, an immense amount of satisfaction in the thought that, after so many years of research, we have at last been able to see with our own eyes a human being in a state of development so far down in the mammalian scale that our affinities with the lower animals must be apparent to even the most prejudiced observer.

We may be curious at this point to learn what Dr. Broom and Dr. Dart think about the possible appearance in life of their wonderful discoveries. To the writer, any plausible conception of such a creature is exceedingly vague. Were we sure that he possessed the power to really walk erect, the problem would be somewhat easier, but that attitude is by no means a certainty until the manlike pelvis is counted as part of the creature's anatomy.

In the matter of features and facial expression we are again in doubt because of the rather hazy indications of the nasal regions which, as Dr. Broom remarks, are perhaps a bit more manlike than those of a chimpanzee. As far as features are concerned, the size and shape of the nose is always a difficult point to consider in any mammal because the general position of the fleshy nostril, which can give so much character to the face, is not indicated except in a very indefinite way. The actual shape of these fleshy nostrils and also the size and shape of the tip of the nose are almost impossible to infer from the bony skeleton alone. Dr. Broom's tentative restoration of the facial profile shows a slight protuberance at the end of the nose, but he is noncommittal in the matter of the nostril. He also draws slightly thickened lips as an approach to the human type, and a deep receding chin. He is probably correct in his surmise about the facial angle, but one confesses to a rather helpless feeling of inadequacy in trying to make anything more than a very nebulous picture of the life appearance of this extraordinary creature. We can not doubt, nevertheless, that there *was* a difference between its general features and that of a chimpanzee or gorilla.

As to its entire form, there again the data is practically nil, and without certain bones such as the femur and humerus to give us clues to the leg and arm lengths, our knowledge at present is sadly deficient. The writer has very often been surprised in his restorations of extinct animal forms to see how easily mistakes can be made unless the entire skeleton is available for measurement and study. One can only hope that time and good luck will help Dr. Broom and his associates to unearth at least the more important bones of this singular being because they will then be able to tell us many things as yet unknown to the world of science. Will *Plesianthropus* have short legs and long arms as do the great apes, or will those appendages be fashioned like those of a man? At present we don't know, but live in a state of interested expectancy for the answer to this fascinating question.

Although our ability to visualize the true life proportions of this unusual mammal is, for the reasons already stated, distinctly limited, we can provisionally imagine in a general way the environment wherein it dwelt in those far-off days of prehuman adolescence. In trying to decide an approximate geological date for the advent of the remarkable creature, scientists have run across some baffling snags owing to the unstratified condition of the rocks and soil which covered the remains. A million years perhaps, say some, while others are convinced that a much more recent rating would be nearer to the truth.

In any case, the animal bones found near by and closely associated with *Plesianthropus* are not extremely old or primitive types, which one might logically expect under the circumstances. No one knows the reason for this discrepancy, but the facts remain to puzzle the trained observer. This being the case, the inference would be that as the animal life resembled that of the present day, the general appearance of the countryside might also have been quite similar to the existing landscape—a semiarid region with many rocks and sparse vegetation, perhaps with caves and other convenient dwelling places separated by clumps of trees, and food enough for a fairly large population.

Exactly what that diet might have been, we do not know, but we can come pretty close to the truth if we are acquainted with the life habits of a chimpanzee or gorilla. These active and powerful creatures are practically vegetarians when in a natural state. Gorillas consume great quantities of bamboo shoots as their *pièce-de-résistance* in the daily regime. Undoubtedly they are able to procure other substances of an agreeably varied nature—grubs, birds' eggs, fruits, nuts, roots, berries, leaves, but never flesh which they kill as do the carnivora. All in all, one might say a not too nutritious diet, but it seems to produce and agree with the vast bulk of a male gorilla, some five hundred pounds of bone and muscle, not to mention a very cantankerous and irascible disposition, which is a part of his ferocious make-up.

The variation in tooth structure between *Plesianthropus* and the great apes is so slight that the diet must have been practically the same in both creatures. However, in the manner of procuring that food, certain differences might be evident, especially if our early ancestor had already acquired a large and more opposable thumb than that of the big monkeys, whose actual grasping powers are limited by the smallness and shortness of that digit. This enlarged thumb gives a very tenacious grip to the human hand and assists him materially in seizing any object such as a stick or a stone with which to repel or attack an adversary. In this connection, there have recently been found at Sterkfontein a number of fossil baboon skulls, each with a small hole broken through near the brain case, apparently the result of a powerful stroke by some blunt instrument. The mystery has so far not been explained satisfactorily, though it is thought by some anthropologists to be the work of a relatively human assailant armed with a heavy pointed stone or wooden club. Whatever its origin, the blow was probably a lethal one and presupposes a certain method of killing these agile and ferocious animals perhaps as they emerged in a dazed condition from some smoke-filled cave. This supposition is, of course, conditional, but it serves, so far, as the only explanation of this singular phenomenon.

It is reasonable to suppose also that, inasmuch as *Plesianthropus* does show in the formation of its skull and face and teeth some slight departure from these same features in its apelike relatives, even in those early days there were glimmerings in its physiognomy and general carriage which suggested possible future manlike proclivities. In other words, we simply *had* to start somewhere in our history to branch off and get away from the very ancient pattern of our still earlier forbears. The extremely ancient apes may have been more generalized than their living descendants, gorilla, chimpanzee, etc., and lived at different periods in widely separated parts of the world. India in particular developed diverse species all with potentialities for advancement into the subhuman class, and *Dryopithecus* extended even as far west as Spain. The world was apparently being prepared for our appearance, but nature meanwhile was to supply many types of mammal whose peculiarities of construction contained the germ of such an eventuality.

Since thus far in our explorations nothing else so

significant in the way of ancestral man has come to
light, *Plesianthropus* and his possibilities are being
very carefully scrutinized by the scientific profession
because they open up whole vistas far down the years
of our ancient lineage when the human side of life
was first beginning to take root in the story of created
things. Perhaps that vision may help us greatly to
understand some of the deeper and still hidden secrets of our own personalities, a most profound and
difficult study but one which, after all, concerns the
entire life of humanity. Certainly we shall not see
in that distant landscape a being exactly akin to our
present-day selves, fully upright, the head hair
sharply differentiated from that covering all the rest
of the body, a prominent well-marked nose, long
legs, short arms, and fingers and toes like our own.
Rather might we discern him scuttling swiftly about,
partially erect, but covered from head to heel with
hair, a stick or stone held tightly in his powerful
hands. Thus armed we visualize him beating a companion, or striking down a running animal by repeated blows, just as a man might do today. The
picture may be imaginary, yet somewhere along the
line of our early existence things must have happened in this way—because the aggressive and well-
armed primate had evolved into a type of creature
which even in its early stages was slowly beginning
to assume its position of world mastery.

It may be that in the South African fields of exploration we have at last stumbled upon the actual remains of these early adventurers, and that as the years go by, more and more interesting finds will further intrigue and clarify our understanding of these lowly but yet potentially manlike beings. There is also the possibility that in Africa we shall come across more highly developed species whose human traits and conformation will be distinctly more apparent. Some sort of link or connection may yet be made along the northern shore of the great continent with such definitely human types as the men of the great Neanderthal and Cro-Magnon peoples who figure so largely in European prehistory.

GIGANTOPITHECUS (*The Chinese Giant*)

The peoples of this world, both ancient and modern, have always been keenly interested in supernatural beings very much larger and stronger than themselves. Humanity apparently loves thrills—while at the same time they are inherently afraid of anything they cannot fully understand. The mythical race of giants, purely imaginary creatures of vast proportions, are still in high favor among certain backward civilizations who, perhaps, see in these unearthly monsters a personification of their own ego expressed in terms of ruthless power and free-

dom from repression. So persistent is this inherited
trait that we may be quite sure our long-haired cave
man ancestors conjured up all sorts of titanic forms
and devilish personalities who lay in wait for miserable humans and harassed them on all possible occasions. It is, therefore, not to be wondered at that
such a mental attitude was prevalent among the
earlier inhabitants of this old world, where terrible
things might and did happen at all too frequent
intervals.

Nevertheless, while correct in their assertions as
to the impossibility of a supernatural giant, even our
present-day savants were, until a few years ago,
unaware of the fact that a veritable race of giant men
had once existed on this earth, and that the proof
of this astonishing statement was on the point of
discovery in (of all places) the chemists' shops of
Hong Kong, China. For on a certain day in 1935 a
young and enthusiastic scientist connected with the
Geological Survey of the Netherlands East Indies
came across the crowns of several enormous molar
teeth, which at the time he thought belonged to some
apelike creature of unusual proportions. Dr. Von
Koenigswald had for some time been poking about
among the many animal remains to be found in the
apothecary establishments of the celestial city, and
had already purchased a number of fossilized teeth
belonging to various species of mammals no longer

in existence in that part of the world. He knew by
experience that these relics were called Dragon's
Bones by the Chinese physicians and that they considered them a powerful specific against disease. The
patient, if he could afford the high prices charged
for these precious remedies, was given a dose of
ground-up bones or teeth in sufficient quantity to
practically guarantee recovery from whatever ailed
him at the moment. But these great teeth were different—so much larger than any he had seen before
that they naturally focused his attention and puzzled
him at the same time. They must be identified, if
possible, and by an expert on the subject. But Von
Koenigswald himself did not at the moment feel
equal to the task; his data was not sufficient, nor
had he had much experience in this difficult field.
Nevertheless, the great teeth worried him because
he felt that there was something remarkable about
them. They were so large and yet they did not closely
resemble those of any great ape, but there was a suggestion of human grinders in a rather vague way.
Could it be that, after all, they *were* human teeth,
that some vast creature hitherto unknown was the
original owner of the gigantic ivories? The whole
thing seemed a bit absurd, almost fantastic, yet Von
Koenigswald could not get it out of his mind.

Meanwhile in Java, Von Koenigswald's white
associates, assisted by some skilled Malay collectors,

were busily hunting for remains of fossil creatures in various parts of the big island. Good luck attended these intensive diggings, and many human skull fragments, lower jaws, and teeth of undoubtedly human origin had come to light and were being carefully assembled for future study. Among these treasures were two or three very thick skulls with heavy brow ridges and low retreating foreheads. Slowly but surely the case for a race of large proportions, which had once lived in China and Java, grew more and more complete. A tooth here, a jaw there, bits of a gigantic skull, or a piece of huge shinbone all pointed to types of humanity perhaps new to paleontologists. In 1939 Von Koenigswald went to Peking, there to meet Dr. Franz Weidenreich of the Rockefeller Institute staff, an acknowledged world expert in the study of prehistoric man. By a careful comparison of Von Koenigswald's material with that of the Peking man remains, some very important deductions were made as to the possible relationships among all the specimens examined. But it was not until 1941, when a section of an enormous jaw was sent in by the Javanese collectors, that our two scientists really admitted to themselves, and to the world in general, the probability of a very early race of human beings so gigantic that they might easily have been the owners of a set of ivories on a scale with the vast grinders of the Hong Kong apothecary shops. The

announcement was almost revolutionary, and it fell
like a bombshell into the ranks of that great army
of scientists who had always attested the impossibility of such a state of affairs. But the statement,
coming as it did from a man of Dr. Weidenreich's
reputation, could not be easily refuted or set aside;
and so, at long last, we had a real honest to goodness
human giant, not much of him, of course, just a few
teeth in an apothecary shop and the jaw section from
another possible giant found in Java, but now we
felt sure that he could be as big as his teeth seemed
to indicate, bigger than any modern man and even
larger than the other races of early men who succeeded him. And the joke of it all was that the remains of our veritable earth-growing giant had lain
buried in the sands and soil of far-eastern countries
ages before the mythical giants who had so tor-
mented our harassed ancestors were even imagined.

The whole affair was a real poser for the scientific
world and naturally it was bound to let loose a storm
of controversy. In fact, some well-known authorities,
even at this date, refuse to admit that the finds necessarily prove that *all* man's primitive ancestors were
gargantuan in proportions, and to such an opinion
the writer of this article subscribes most heartily.
My own feeling is that the giant-ancestor idea seems
to quite reverse the usual story as shown in the evolution of prehistoric life in general. Because in many

lines of development noticeable among ancient animal families it seems that the various groups as a rule began in a small way, growing larger and more highly specialized in succeeding geological periods, until they had attained a maximum of certain characteristics, both as to size and shape. Such well-known progressions as those of the elephant, the horse, the camel, and many other forms still in existence, all show this trend in the course of their long life histories. Again, it is quite possible that the proud possessor of the big molars might have belonged to a race of men who had been born in a particularly favorable environment for bodily development. Good food and plenty of it, freedom from molestation, though this is a difficult thing to conceive in a wild creature, a salubrious climate and plenty of space to wander about—all these advantages will strongly influence the growth of any animal species, even at the present day. We also know, from actual finds of fossil types, that certain lines of animal evolution seem to follow along prescribed paths of development and that many of them, after reaching what appears to be the limit for a particular class in the way of horns and tusks, general bulk and other characters, have a tendency to show a reduction in all these special features. The elephant life story is a splendid example of what is meant in this connection as we have a tremendously long line of pachyderms on which to found our assertions. From the quite small elephantlike ancestors which once existed in Egypt, we may trace the family through succeeding ages and in various parts of the world— India, Africa, Europe, and North and South America. Many and varied are the types, but as the ages passed, the intelligent creatures, for the most part, seemed to grow larger and larger, until they had, in the great Mammoths of our own country and those of Europe and Asia, attained gigantic size with huge curved tusks fifteen feet or more in length, and bodies in proportion. However, after the lapse of ages, the evolution of any family may become of secondary importance in nature's great plan, with the result that today neither the African nor Indian elephants are the equal of the big long-tusked Mammoths which once wandered over large sections of the earth's surface. It may be, therefore, that man himself attained his greatest physical bulk and stature in the creature which is the subject of this section (*Gigantopithecus blacki*). If so, then the modern races of men do appear to be decreasing in physical stature but their mental equipment has advanced in quite the opposite direction. The extraordinary superiority of man's intelligence is naturally an outstanding phenomenon, but it is a fact exceedingly difficult to explain. It may be, however, that the seeds of man's ultimate destruction are concealed

beneath that brilliant exterior. Too much brain may
be even more dangerous than too little, and an intelligence run wild, without the possibility of curbing
its exuberance, has recently brought us to a terrible
and ominous impasse in our struggle for supremacy.

The foregoing remarks are not intended to be
unduly pessimistic; they merely state facts impossible
to cast aside, and are simply the natural results of a
careful survey of man's past history. For with the
discovery of the great molars of our presumable
giant, a new and truly revealing life chapter became
apparent. How did this great creature fit into the
story already known to scientific men—how big could
he really have been when standing erect, and what
was his general appearance? Mighty interesting
questions these, and all difficult to answer. So meager
is our information on these early human types that
even trained paleontologists must assemble all possible data in order to arrive at any definite conclusions concerning their physical formation. Every
known type of prehistoric man, both late and early,
must be carefully compared with any new finds in
whatever part of the world they are discovered.
Naturally, men like Weidenreich and Von Koenigswald must be fully aware of all such discoveries and
have in their minds very clear impressions of the
important characteristics concerning them. As most
of the data on prehistoric man consists largely of

skulls partially perfect and lower jaws and teeth, these sections of the anatomy are all examined with the most minute care for resemblances and differences in form, size, time sequence, zoological environment, and distribution.

Thus far in our discussions we have merely hinted at the possible appearance in life of the *Gigantopithecus*. The illustrations on pages 16 and 17 will perhaps convey better than any written description the author's ideas on the subject, and they represent only a personal conception of the size and presumable appearance of the Chinese superman in the heyday of his existence, believing him to have been of stocky build, broad bodied, rather short in limb, and big rather than small headed. On this supposition, the fellow need not have been over seven feet tall, but with a vast depth and breadth of body unknown among the present-day giants of our own species. His weight could not have been under six hundred, perhaps seven hundred pounds. A definitely giant man in every way, and no doubt strong and not too amiable in temperament. In fact, he might easily have been the model from which our more recent ancestors built up their own supernatural big man, with all his great size, fierceness, and generally sinister characteristics multiplied a hundred times in a lip to lip heritage of many thousands of years. However, in spite of bulk and brawn, *Gigantopithecus* seemed a true man and not of the gorilla type, but rather like an overgrown Neanderthal—the European representative of a much later but still extremely primitive race of prehistoric humans.

As for the present-day gorilla, a comparison in size and weight to our *Gigantopithecus* shows the latter to have been superior in both these attributes. Gorillas in captivity have been known to attain a weight of 640 pounds; for example, the San Diego Zoo specimen who died a few years ago, but he was considered vastly overweight at the time of his demise. At present, the magnificent male "Bushman" in the Chicago Zoo tips the scales at 550 pounds, is not overfat, and stands six feet two inches in his bare feet—a truly superb creature in every way, but dour and dangerous in the extreme. Bushman, however, is all ape and distinctly not of the human type. Yet he has many manlike characteristics, intermingled with his more simian proclivities.

The Chinese prodigy, as indicated, is big all over, not merely an over-sized human type, with long, weak, gangling proportions and a too small head for his body. As for intelligence, even in the distant days when *Gigantopithecus* ruled the forests of his native China, and his huge relatives in Java were fighting and feeding and dying in their leafy solitudes, his mentality was superior to that of any gorilla. Already the urge to progress mentally and the potential power to do so are evident in the increasing brain capacity of the various manlike races under discussion, and this ever-increasing ratio of brain to body size has continued until the present day. What future discoveries may disclose along the lines of man's development, we cannot say. New races and types will undoubtedly come to light under the intensive efforts of scientific experts in the field. They will, however, in our opinion merely augment our present knowledge of the subject without vitally altering the main conclusions regarding man's earlier development and his various affinities with other mammals of closely related stocks. These extraordinary finds are but a few of the links in the chain which serves to connect the present human animal with a very long line of still more primitive creatures whose origin extends far back into the mists of antiquity.

PITHECANTHROPUS ERECTUS

In all the annals of the search for the remains of prehistoric man, no discovery is more unusual and interesting than the finding of *Pithecanthropus* in the wilds of Java in 1891. The fossil was brought to light by a young Dutch scientist, Eugene Dubois, who it appears had become obsessed with the idea of an Eastern environment for our earliest human

types. Dubois had conceived this notion after read-
ing the works of Darwin and Huxley on the subject
of evolution in general, and he argued that, on
account of certain similarities in climatic and faunal
conditions both in India and the Eastern Archi-
pelago, the Island of Java might prove an ideal site
for his research work. Fortunately for the young
enthusiast, he was able to secure a commission as
medical doctor for the Dutch Government in the
Indies and was later transferred to Java, there to
continue his hunt for prehistoric man.

In October of 1891 near Trinil on the Solo River,
he came upon the flattened skullcap of a primitive
creature which he presumed was related, though
remotely, to the human class of mammals. In the
following year, a femur—long, slim, straight, and
almost recent in general appearance—was unearthed
in the near vicinity of the skullcap. Dubois, rightly
or wrongly, claimed a close relationship between
the two fossil relics.

This really was an epochal event in anthropological
history, because at the time it seemed to indicate the
very earliest stage of human development. The world
rang with conflicting voices raised for and against
the antiquity and meaning of these two insignificant
pieces of bone. Dubois, however, was of stubborn
stature, and he remained unmoved by all the fracas
and the turmoil engendered by his new discovery,

keeping his two precious relics closely guarded from prying scientific eyes and studying with expert care and deliberation the strange form and contour of his priceless fossil. He wrote treatises about it as well in which he dealt at length with all the finer details as he saw them, and slowly but surely he built up a classic bit of scientific investigation which was entirely his own in every way. Naturally the professional world was agog with curiosity to see this ancient fragment and to handle and examine it to their hearts' content. But Dubois set his face strongly against all such familiarity, and his rare and unique find was kept closely boxed and hidden beneath his bed. On very rare occasions some favored soul was granted a near view of the wonderful fragment of bony skull, as well as the brown and shiny femur or thigh bone with its bit of extraneous contour projecting strangely from the shaft just below the rounded upper end of the femur itself.

What was the story behind those two pieces of fragile construction? Did they demonstrate to us for the first time that men of a race far different and much lower in the human scale than ourselves had lived several hundred thousand years ago in the steamy Javan forests? They certainly did all that insofar as the material went because the projection of skullcap was, in its elevation above the bony eye ridges, somewhere between that of a gorilla and a modern man. Nothing like this had ever been seen before, and many thought that science was here treading on dangerous ground in more ways than one. It simply couldn't be authentic, this strangely shaped top of an old-time skull, because it somehow suggested to the observer a kind of monkeylike mentality, and speculations in that direction were at the time distinctly fraught with dynamite for the average man. Thus the fracas went on for years among professionals. The public more or less forgot about the whole matter in the tremendous press of world events forever attracting their attention. Science, of course, never forgets such things because topics and discoveries of this description are the very lifeblood of an intensive search for the truth in all things.

While Professor Dubois' find proved to be a new, interesting subject for comparison with the remains of other types of early man, yet the data was so meager, consisting of the skullcap and femur only, that there came a time when, outside of careful conjecture and a most exhaustive study of the remains, very little more could be said upon the subject. A certain Mme. Selenka had subsequently made a special visit to the Trinil district, but her search though intensive had yielded practically no results, and *Pithecanthropus* remained a tremendously interesting but static bit of paleontological evidence.

There was, of course, still the hope that another hunt for more complete data on the subject would be instigated and prove successful. Meanwhile, Professor Dubois' treasure remained carefully sequestered from professional inspection even though the world of science kept its anthropological ears cocked for any such eventuality. And the *Pithecanthropus* aura became less and less visible as time went on, its glory somewhat eclipsed by other finds in other places.

But in 1937 and 1938, events again began to take shape in the old Trinil River region of Java. For several years previous to these dates, a young Dutch anthropologist, Von Koenigswald, and his confreres had been carefully searching various sites in the big island for possible fossils of *Pithecanthropus* or other very early examples of prehuman stock. They were all young fellows, these Dutch enthusiasts, keen, ambitious, and able to withstand the difficult climatic conditions of the country. Many natives were drawn into the search, some of them showing marked ability as collectors, and results were soon forthcoming in several selected localities.

Numbers of bones of fossil animals—elephants, hippopotamus, buffalo, deer, rhinoceros, and others —were thus incidentally disclosed, showing that a large and various fauna had once existed in the region. *Pithecanthropus* had been obliged to share its

shaded forest fastnesses with a host of other powerful
and dangerous creatures. These he no doubt cleverly
avoided whenever possible, seeking no encounters
with such formidable adversaries. The Netherlands
coterie eventually also unearthed many large and
small fragments of several skulls and other bones
pertaining to early humans in the district. Sections
of jaws with practically uninjured teeth showed the
peculiar deep receding chin of the Neanderthal man
of Europe, but in a more exaggerated form. The
skulls themselves were unique in the extreme thickness of the bony brain case, as well as in certain
other characteristics hitherto but little appreciated.
The finds thus described were not essentially *Pithecanthropus* in detail, and have been ascribed to another species known as the Solo Man of an almost
equal antiquity. So the search continued, and in 1937
Von Koenigswald and his helpers were fortunate
in finding what they considered a very fine skullcap of
a true *Pithecanthropus* fossil. The collectors were
overjoyed and amazed at the extremely close resemblance in shape between their latest find and that
brought to light by Dubois fifty-seven years before.
The new skull portion was more complete than the
earlier example, particularly in certain very important characteristics, and combined with the lower
jaw (unknown to Dubois) we were at last able to
visualize with tolerable accuracy the appearance of

the entire bony framework of the head in this remarkable species of ancient humanity.

In this connection we are pleased to recount a real anatomical triumph of scientific deduction accomplished by an expert. Some years ago, Dr. J. H. McGregor of Columbia University essayed a series of restorations (based on the evidence of the fossil remains) of various prehistoric man types—Neanderthal, Cro-Magnon, Piltdown, and finally *Pithecanthropus*. The remains were all carefully measured and evaluated while various estimates of skin thickness, nose form and projection, eye position, size and probable expression, profile of chin and skull were undertaken to help Dr. McGregor in his difficult task. Already, the entire skull and jaw of both Neanderthal and Cro-Magnon man were definitely known, but at the time, 1913 or 1914, only the skullcap and the femur of *Pithecanthropus* had been retrieved by Dubois.

Thus handicapped, Dr. McGregor set out to reconstruct a lower jaw and set of teeth for the Trinil fossil which should have what he, as an osteologist, conceived to be the correct form and proportion for this section of the creature's head. The result was most convincing, yet there was still no actual proof of its accuracy. But when Von Koenigswald years later was able to construct from his finds the veritable shape of the jaw itself, McGregor's model was seen to be a singularly close replica of the original. Thus by a combination of art and anatomical knowledge the scientist had again indicated the surprising value of inferential conclusions when based on a profound knowledge of all the probabilities and possibilities inherent in the evidence. As has been said, this does not mean that all reconstructions of other types of extinct creatures would be equally successful if accomplished in this manner. The instance is cited here not only to give an expert due appreciation, but also to emphasize the fact that man and his relatives have for ages been singularly conservative as to the type of change brought about in the skeleton by environmental and evolutionary forces. Whether *Pithecanthropus* was able to produce fire or to make artifacts is not known, but he may nevertheless have possessed the brain power to appreciate the value of a stick or a stone as a weapon, and the use of these two implements must have been an almost instinctive characteristic of ancient man. It has been supposed that this lowly being might almost have been able to make articulate sounds and perhaps had a kind of language which enabled him to communicate with his fellows. Whether he was timid or aggressive we cannot say, but the chances are that he was cunning and far more clever than the great apes of his day and time.

HEIDELBERG MAN

In 1907 a lower jaw complete with teeth, apparently that of some manlike creature, was found at the bottom of an eighty-foot sand pit near Mauer in the vicinity of Heidelberg. As described by Schoetensack, it was huge, massively constructed, and possessed a heavy, deep but receding chin, something quite new to science at the time. Naturally the experts went busily to work upon this extraordinary object as all had to admit that in spite of its size and peculiar shape it couldn't, on account of its distinctly manlike dentition, be anything but human. What the skull was like, no one could say, but the creature must have been a powerfully built, brutish-looking fellow of considerable bulk and fair stature.

This find was one of great antiquity. The manlike creature must have lived during the second interglacial age, perhaps 200,000 to 350,000 years ago; but thus far no other specimen of its kind has been exposed. The great thickness and depth of the bone structure of the jaw could have belonged only to a being with a powerful bite and coarse protruding face. The teeth are rather small and set very evenly in the form of a horseshoe, unlike the apes whose molars run almost parallel to each other on opposite sides of the mouth. In 1907, neither Peking man nor the lower jaw of *Pithecanthropus,* the Java ape man,

Early man attacking the great cave bear

Neanderthal man defending his family from a wolf pack

had been discovered, so that the excessively massive character of the fossil created a great amount of interest and speculation. Today, however, the anthropologist has come to recognize in this powerful jaw a type of bony structure inherent in such early manlike creatures as *Pithecanthropus* and the Peking race, where it is associated with an equally primitive skull formation—heavy brow ridges, a long, low top to the head, a flat, broad nose, and the apelike chin, all characteristic of the lower branches of our ancestral tree.

But there are often inconsistencies in the skeletal structure of any animal and had not the rather small teeth of the Heidelberg man been in place when found, we may be sure that scientists would have imagined a much larger set as indicated by the jaw itself. Indeed, most other early races do show just such big ivories both in the upper and lower jaws. We may speculate about this phenomenon, but thus far neither the skull nor any part of Heidelberg man has come to light, though the solitary jaw is of great interest because it proves a past antiquity for primitive man in the European field.

PILTDOWN MAN (*Eoanthropus*)

In 1911 an English geologist, Charles Dawson, found pieces of a very thick skull of human type in a shallow bed of gravel which was being used in local road-building operations. As an expert, he was at once impressed by the peculiar nature of this discovery and straightway elicited the help of his friend Arthur Smith Woodward, himself a paleontologist of note. Together, they very carefully sorted large amounts of scattered material, and at length came across the right half of a jaw which presumably might have belonged with the pieces of skull already unearthed. Fossilized remains of several interesting mammals—a mastodon, elephants of various types, a water vole, rhinoceros, beaver, a deer's leg bone, and a hippopotamus—were associated with the human relics. A single flint of a very early type was also recovered, and later two large pieces of animal bone, sharpened to a point, the first of this type on record.

As so often in the past, this discovery was like a new fagot cast upon the great controversial fire, and the flames burst forth afresh as the scientific world sought to evaluate the merits and the discrepancies of the new discovery. The hottest ember in this intellectual conflagration proved to be the section of the jaw already referred to. Indeed there was room for discussion here because of the strangely simian or apelike shape of this important part of the ancient creature's anatomy. The scientific battlers at once ranged themselves, some for, others against the supposition that the jaw had ever belonged to the skull even though both had been lying in the almost identical spot in the gravel pit.

It can easily be realized by those familiar with similar claims which have been made from time to time that here was a fit subject for a most exciting line of discussion among paleontologists, anatomists, geologists, and anthropologists, and this formidable array of *"ists"* proceeded to thoroughly enjoy themselves around their traditional campfire. Of course, owing to the fragmentary nature of the find, attempts at restoration of the skull and the accompanying jaw began at once with the result that a head finally was built up in what was thought to be the correct life form of this early human physiognomy. The work naturally was criticized, especially in this country where the evidence was thoroughly sifted, and again Dr. J. H. McGregor of Columbia, who had already embarked upon the reconstruction of the Javan *Pithecanthropus* head, attempted a separate and different build-up of the scattered bits of the Piltdown skull. Over these when completed he reconstructed a modeled form of his idea of the creature's head as it might have appeared in life.

As usual the effect is convincingly real, but alas, today in scientific circles *Eoanthropus* or the Dawn Man has suffered somewhat of a relapse from his former prominent position in the hierarchy of early man. This change is not to be wondered at, because after all the contour of the skull was something unique in man's early history, appearing strangely like a modern man or woman on account of its up-right profile, the roundness of the skull, and the lack of the heavy brow ridges so commonly associated with other types of ancient people. Here again, we simply don't know. As this unusual being seems to indicate, perhaps there once was another type and race whose face didn't appear quite so gorilla-like in its general contour as do those of the Neanderthal, Java, and Peking groups of primitive humans.

CHOU-KOU-TIEN (*Peking Man*)

The story of the finding of *Sinanthropus Pekin-ensis* (the Chinese man of Peking) is a complicated and intriguing one extending over a period of years and participated in by scientists of various nationali-ties. It all began when, in 1903, a tooth was sent from Peking to Professor Schlosser, a German ex-pert who promptly recognized in the fossil something suggestive of an ancient type of human being from the Peking area.

Much serious research was being carried on in China in the early years of this century, and a number of able men, among them Professor Davidson Black of the Geological Survey of China, were convinced that somewhere in the neighborhood of the Imperial

City an actual skull or skeleton might be found which would prove quite new to science and be of great assistance in the study of fossil man. We may imagine then with what satisfaction Dr. Black received the good news that, in December, 1929, his assistant, a certain Dr. Pei, had discovered in a cave near the village of Chou-Kou-Tien, a very complete brain case of an altogether primitive type of human being, and that the specimen was being brought to him in Peking. This cave, situated in the western hills about forty miles distant from the Imperial City, was extremely difficult to excavate, and it had taken all of Dr. Pei's oriental persistence to accomplish the final excellent result.

Here was indeed a wholly new anthropological treasure of the very first importance, and under Dr. Black's skillful treatment, the skullcap was freed on the inside from a mass of hard gritty stone, and a plaster cast taken of the hollowed section. This operation which naturally resulted in a model of the brain itself was an invaluable bit of technical work, and one which has vastly augmented our knowledge of the cerebral development of early human beings. A comparison with the *Pithecanthropus* skullcap and the Piltdown head seemed to place the new find somewhere between these two types, but several American scientists later professed a belief that Peking man showed certain Neanderthal affinities, a conclusion which a close examination of the two skulls appears to verify.

Since 1929, several unusually complete skulls and jaws and other bones of the Peking fossils have been recovered from their ancient mortuary which also contains large numbers of animal remains of different species—rhinoceros, tigers, deer, cattle, elephants, and a host of others which had existed contemporaneously or before or after *Sinanthropus*. All in all the find was epochal in its revelation of many interesting problems. For our purposes, it is evident that here was a type of creature which, though lowly and undeveloped in many ways, was yet a stage above the Javan ape man and that at last he had begun the tremendously long climb upward towards a veritable human type. What lay ahead of this thick-skulled creature, he could not in any way have imagined, nor has science yet found his geographical position in the Chinese region easy to explain. We still do not know the complete figure of this neo-human being, whether he was tall or short, stocky or slim, though we may infer a kind of generalized stature for him, some conformation by which he was able to exist under possibly very strenuous climatic conditions.

Prehistorically, perhaps, he anticipated the late Horace Greeley's sage advice, "Go west, young man," and was the first creature of a human type to turn his grim face toward the sunset. Whether on that immensely long migration the races of developing man stopped in India, or other central Asian regions, we can not as yet say although presumably such arrested journeys did take place. In any case, long ages were to intervene and man was to advance greatly before we again meet him on his way across the continents of Asia and Europe. There are those in the world of science who claim a central Asian origin for the races of man, and they can point directly to several well-advanced apelike creatures whose remains have been found in India, where all such fundamental forms could of course be possible providing one went back far enough into the realm of antiquity.

MT. CARMEL CAVES NEAR JERUSALEM

When next we pick up the trail of our very ancient ancestors, they will appear thousands of miles from the Peking area of China and the Chou-Kou-Tien cave near the great city. The forces of time and environment have left their mark upon these wanderers, changing in certain ways their general physique by improving their brain capacity and very likely altering the bodily form. Whether the remains unearthed by Miss Dorothy Garrod and

T. D. McCown in the Mt. Carmel region of the Holy Land, in 1929, bear any but a general relationship to Peking man, we have no means of knowing. Certainly the skeletons belong to a unique type of human being, but the variation is not so great as we might suppose, considering the much greater antiquity of the Peking specimens. In fact, one of the strangest things about man is the extreme slowness with which any changes occur in his general anatomy and bodily proportions.

It is evident from a rather casual examination of the extensive Mt. Carmel material, which consists of numerous skeletons, that not one but *two* types of human beings are here represented, a kind of crossing or interbreeding of two races: the lowly Neanderthal variety and a more highly developed people, some of a possible Cro-Magnon type, both of which are superior to the Peking race. Hitherto, no such interbreeding had been observed in the history of these two stocks, certainly not in the European area where the pure Neanderthals preceded the Cro-Magnons and apparently lived for ages in undisputed possession of the cave sites and rock shelters.

In addition, the great caves at Mt. Carmel proved a spectacular storehouse of fossilized bones of both men and animals, which had occupied the grottoes through a long period of time. The lower layers of the deposit indicated a warm and moist climate where the hippopotamus, rhinoceros, and elephant were at home, to be succeeded in later ages by a series of animals—gazelles, wild asses, wart hogs and others—which indicated an almost desert fauna. These in turn gave way to horses, wild boar, deer of various species, wild cattle, and bears, almost a specifically European series. The upper strata of this great deposit comprise the times of modern man, and numerous articles of manufacture attest his presence there until practically our own day.

NEANDERTHAL MAN

Whatever we may infer from the discovery of the apparently mixed Neanderthal-Cro-Magnon inhabitants of the Mt. Carmel cave, it is advantageous to realize that with the advent of the pure Neander people in eastern Europe we are in possession of some very important facts concerning the exact form and proportions of one of our earlier relatives. This was indeed a turning point in man's physical and mental development, where a very ancient combination of almost human attributes at last reached its final expression. The long flattened head, heavy brow ridges, projecting face, and deep receding chin so characteristic of the Java man and the Peking race are still evident in the skull profile of the Neanderthal man. But certain modifications of these primitive characters indicate a possible change to a more refined skeletal conformation. Apparently the very ancient man type was no longer desirable for the human race, and the crude and roughly fashioned being who for ages had withstood all of life's vicissitudes was relegated to the almost mythical past in man's long existence upon our planet. We knew that Neanderthal man had developed from this earlier type because so many ancient characteristics are present in his form.

In 1908 not only the skull, but the complete skeleton of this definitely antique being were found in a grotto near La Chapelle-aux-Saints in France. Skulls and parts of skeletons in practically perfect condition have, as we have said, been known for some years to members of the anthropological profession, but the exhuming of a wonderfully complete skeleton (that of an old man) at once placed the experts in possession of the first real data concerning the bulk, proportions, standing height, and posture of the Neanderthal type. He was a short, stocky, rugged individual, some 5 feet 4 inches in height, big-headed and clumsy, with a short neck, not especially long arms, big hands and feet, and shorter than any modern man below the knee. All in all, he was just what we might have expected of such an ancient creature, but now we had actual proof in the study of the bones themselves. A very resistant individual physically, and though not endowed with the highest type of brain power, he was intelligent, a fighter, and aided by his tools and weapons an accomplished hunter of big game.

It is probable that Neanderthal man arrived in western Europe at some time during the earlier stages of the fourth and last glacial epoch and that the climate was then comparatively warm, a fact which we judge by the presence of certain species of his animal contemporaries. These were all definitely southern types, such as elephants, hippopotamus, and others, which had apparently wandered far from their original habitat in the vast regions south of the Mediterranean Sea. Later, however, these seem to vanish or retreat, unable to withstand the increasing cold of the great glaciers which were then slowly engulfing many parts of the northern regions of Europe. The temperatures began to drop and the humidity increased as the tongues of ice crept down into the valleys from the mountain regions now covered by immense falls of snow.

Neanderthal man was hard put to it in those frigid years. He was obliged to rely more and more upon the protection afforded by a retreat to the caves and rock shelters of his dreary habitat. Now he built great fires, hunted big game, fought off enemies and everlastingly chipped his heavy, rough flint tools, his hand axes and hammers, and the smaller objects

for boring, skinning animals, and scraping hides.
Existence was doleful enough, but knowing no other,
he was probably satisfied with his lot and lived and
died in a sort of dreadful security, automatically
guarded to some extent by the intensely severe
northern conditions of a midglacial environment.
How long such a chilly haven of refuge existed is
not definitely known, but it continued without question for thousands of years, relieved by periods of
lesser cold. While the animal life varied considerably
with each new temperature fluctuation, the cold-
country fauna followed the glacial retreats and
advances with surprising adaptability to local conditions.

So long as men of a hostile and superior race did
not put in an appearance, these early types were safe
from extinction, but when, as was bound to happen,
the new races eventually made their entry into these
frozen regions the fate of the Neanderthal peoples
was sealed forever. The doughty little men, inured
to natural hardship, could not long withstand the
encroachments of the highly developed Cro-Magnon
tribes who, armed perhaps with spear throwers and
barbed lances, gradually encroached upon the gloomy
cave sites of the Neanderthal inhabitants and forced
them to seek precarious dwelling stations, at times in
bitterly cold and dangerously exposed sections of
their local habitat. Here, unprotected and preyed

upon by hungry carnivora—lions, leopards, wolves, and hyenas and harassed by hostile human enemies, they may have succumbed in a few decades of an increasingly miserable existence.

CRO-MAGNON MAN

The sun of a great new life was rising upon the races of men as they emerged at long last from the chrysalis of an extremely ancient pattern both of mind and body, and in the splendid forms and high intellect of the Cro-Magnon pioneers there lay potentialities of a superior order. Gone forever was the low-browed Neander Valley man—squat, grotesque, savage, and distinctly limited in his capabilities. The go-westward urge so apparent in man's immigrations had at last enabled Cro-Magnon men to reach what is now Czechoslovakia, where numerous remains of their former presence have come to light in the last few years under the expert supervision of Dr. Karl Absolon, a noted anthropologist.

Various early camp and hearth sites have been excavated and fully studied, and many valuable relics —bones of animals, human remains, small sculptures in bone and ivory, and a host of man's later artistic and utilitarian productions in pottery and bronze and other mediums—have increased this superb collection to immense proportions. Among the Cro-

Magnon deposits, a great number of mammoth skeletons were uncovered (the long bones cracked for the marrow), as well as an assemblage of tusks of the unfortunate pachyderms. Some great feast was evidently held at this point, and the fire hearths indicate a nightly gathering of hungry savages, who had cast aside for the time being any yearnings for the higher artistic values and gorged themselves with huge pieces of roasted mammoth flesh.

The route taken by the Cro-Magnons in western Europe can thus be traced through a corridor leading from the eastern world of mystery and a yet unknown source of man's initial development. Somewhere, perhaps in Central Asia, changes took place in our anatomical form which enabled the once lowly Neanderthal and Peking races of humanity to so tremendously advance their personalities and physical status that the truly manlike type as exemplified in the Cro-Magnon people at last became an actuality. For the school of scientific thought which settles upon Africa instead of Asia as man's probable birthplace, this explanation will not suffice. But a study of the whole abstruse subject will leave one in the usual quandary as to which continent may be regarded as our racial cradle and a domicile for our adolescent evolution.

Wherever these events took place, in the Cro-Magnon man as we see him in western Europe there

lay not only the spirit of that artistic genius for which
he is so justly celebrated, but also a growing cultural
enlightenment, a more civilized outlook upon life in
general, and a desire to extend his existence beyond
the limits of the grave. Evidence of this latter urge
may be seen in various interments scattered throughout western Europe. At the Barma Grande caves, for
example, near Menton on the Riviera, several large
skeletons of these people have been excavated, all
showing extreme care and thought in the burial
arrangements. Chaplets of perforated shells surrounded the head, and implements of various types
were placed close at hand presumably for use in some
future state of existence. Although we have reason
to believe that the handsome Cro-Magnon race had
existed in various parts of Europe for thousands of
years, yet as far as we know they never advanced
culturally into the realm of pottery-making, weaving,
or other simple crafts which were to become so vital
to peoples of other types now slowly converging from
several directions upon the western extension of the
European peninsula.

These migrations became more feasible as the
gradually lessening cold of the last great ice age and
the subsequent retreat of the glaciers opened for
travel large sections of the land along the shores of
the Baltic Sea. Apparently the new tribes, the Maglemose races of Denmark, did not intermingle with the

artistic inhabitants of the region to the south, nor do we know the eventual fate of the wonderful Cro-Magnon people. Many theories have been advanced on this subject, some authorities claiming that the Guanches, a very tall cave-living people of the Canary Islands (where they were discovered by the Spaniards in the fifteenth century), might well have been remnants of the Cro-Magnon race. Others profess to see in the Basques of the Pyrenean regions of France and Spain a certain resemblance to these earlier people, particularly in the shape of the head and face. However, all these assumptions seem somewhat vague, not well substantiated and perhaps of doubtful origin.

In any case, the reign of the Cro-Magnon race was on the wane, and the Old Stone Age was at the same time drawing to a close.

ART IN PREHISTORY

The wind blows cold across the hills and vales in a cave man's world, and the icy breath of the nearby glaciers steals through the dark forests of spruce and fir which hug the slopes along the sheltered valley. Deep, turbulent streams swollen by the glacial waters rush madly over the sharp boulders strewn thickly in the heavy current. Summer has passed and the

willows and alders are slowly turning a greenish gold
as the frosty nights of autumn play havoc with their
delicate foliage. Soon the first snow flurries will be
falling, ever more frequent and violent as the year
progresses until the heavy drifts pile high against
the rocks and tree trunks, and great herds of animals
driven from their more open feeding grounds will
file slowly into the quiet reaches of this favored
region.

Huge woolly mammoths, reddish black in color,
with long gleaming tusks curving gracefully before
their waving trunks, will be strolling about or resting
in the wan sunlight, while scattered groups of bison,
reindeer, and horses graze or browse upon the
mosses, grasses, and shrubbery growing along the
exposed slopes at the edge of the forest. At times
some fierce woolly rhinoceros, two-horned and aggressive, causes a mild panic as he lumbers swiftly
into the throngs of game drinking at a quiet pool or
backwash of the river.

High along the face of the great cliffs that rise
steeply from the valley floor, fires are burning here
and there upon the narrow terraces at the base of
the rock shelters. Crowds of people, tall and well
favored, clad in the skins of animals, gather about
the blazing embers, laughing, perhaps even making
articulate sounds as they roast and devour great
pieces of smoking horseflesh, a favorite food in those

far-off days. For this is Southern France some 30,000 years ago when the long Ice Ages were drawing to a close, and these big genial savages belonged to the so-called Cro-Magnon race that, originating in some distant place toward the rising run, had already driven out the scrubby little Neanderthal men who for so long had occupied the country.

In these surroundings the new arrivals, sturdy, handsome, and splendid specimens of a truly human species, will eventually leave behind them in pictures and models, representations of a large series of animal forms whose prototypes they can easily discern from their advantageous eyries below the high outcurving rocks of their chosen dwelling places. For, strangely enough, some of these men possess the unique power of representation, the ability to draw or paint something which has come into the range of their mental and physical vision. Artists, in embryo, and the world's first of which there exists any record. It will not be long before certain individuals of the tribe, specially gifted in this fascinating occupation, will select certain caves and grottoes throughout the region in which to work and produce their wonderful pictures. These caves, of course, if not artificially lighted in some manner, exist in a state of intensely profound darkness, a vital defect which must be overcome before it will be possible to use a portion of some fairly smooth wall or ceiling as a background for any kind of artistic expression. But the Cro-Magnon artist is a resourceful creature trained apparently by long practice to overcome many difficulties, and the problem of lighting he has already solved satisfactorily by the use of tiny stone lamps which, when filled with oil or grease, and the mossy wick set afire by well directed flint-struck sparks, will burn with a faint clear flame. As he could not work and at the same time hold the lamp, there must have been friends or trained apprentices to assist him in his labors; men who skillfully directed the light against any particular section of the long wall upon which the artist wished to delineate his impressions of a series of mammoths, placed head to tail just as he has observed them in the valley below the mouth of the cave. Now, standing before the clearly illuminated but none too even surface of the cavern's side, he begins to carefully incise the outlines of his group of hairy pachyderms with a piece of sharp flint. The hard point, guided by a powerful hand, cuts deeply into the softer wall surface as the impatient man strives to reproduce correctly the profiles and proportions of his models, indicating the great masses of hair upon their heads and shoulders, the long recurved tusks and the little ears and stubby tails of these huge brutes. The work is hard, the light uncertain, and his hand none too accurate (wandering at times from the true outline of the living creatures); but he is enthusiastic, cheered by the appreciation of his friends, and continues his labors until the strange procession of large shaggy creatures seem to follow one another into the blackness at the rear of the cavern.

Everyone is tired by this time, the mossy wicks in the lamps have used up their small amounts of oil and are beginning to smoke and sputter. Slowly the natural gloom of the great cave asserts itself, and the men troop towards the grotto entrance where, seated upon the convenient boulders, they talk, albeit the words may be few and crudely uttered, about their plans for work at another time. There is still much to be done to the mammoth group. An assistant will grind and mix with grease the powdered tints of ochre, some yellow, some red, which when applied to the already outlined drawings of the mammoths will give much life and realism to the artist's creation. The sun is setting now across the valley, the great herds of game are resting or strolling idly about in the sharp clear atmosphere of the oncoming night, and as the tired workers gaze wistfully along cliff fronts, the smoke and flame from the great home fires comfort and reassure these artists of an earlier day. The last golden beams of the sun cast a warm glow upon their strongly marked features and tall powerful forms, then fade slowly out of sight beyond the distant hills. An epic in man's emotional history has taken place in the now silent grotto. The divine spark of a transcendent imagination has left its impression upon the stony walls. The imagery is not overdrawn nor the sentiment unduly accentuated, for without the deep feeling implied in such productions, no such thing as art expression could ever have come into being.

The artistic efforts of the Cro-Magnons were not by any means confined to mural painting and drawing. We find in many different localities, both in eastern and western Europe, evidences of their ability as carvers and sculptors of both human and animal forms. As many of these small figures are quite sophisticated both in subject and treatment, we must infer that we are looking at productions with a fairly long technical history behind them. The models of human figures are quite rare, and usually represent enormously fat women especially developed in the breasts and buttocks, apparently in an effort to symbolize the reproductive and maternal elements of the female form. They have been referred to, not very accurately, as statuettes of a primitive type of Venus, but they are far too gross and overdeveloped to more than faintly resemble the amorous and beautiful goddess. It is possible also that these obese images were really regarded as household idols, bringing good luck in the form of many children or much food to their fortunate possessors. As works of art they are certainly not very convincing, but they do indicate a knowledge of construction and anatomy very remarkable in a people as ancient as the Cro-Magnons.

However, the story is quite a different one where the making of animal models is concerned. The artist evidently derived much inspiration from his observation of the forms and contours of the wildlife of his native region. It is indeed a revelation to note with what skill and ingenuity he carved the little shapes, making them conform to various curved and restricted surfaces such as dagger handles and other implements, as well as tools used either in fighting or for domestic purposes. They often represent, and most interestingly, the heads and bodies of horses, deer, mammoths, and certain birds—all lovingly indicated in excellent character upon bits of bone and ivory, which could only have been used for ornamental purposes. The truly artistic insight shown in the construction and character of the creatures represented speaks well for the keen observation of these ancient people so strongly gifted with this unique form of emotional expression. The acme of this type of work is to be found in the cavern of Tuc. d'Audoubert in Southern France, where two bison, a male and a female modeled in clay, stand forth in full relief as the finest examples of their kind.

The incentives and bases for the demonstration of artistic ability are naturally exceedingly difficult to fathom; particularly because of the abstruse nature of the art impulse. Rather, we have here a mysterious striving for the esthetic production of images impressed upon the mind and vision of certain individuals, an emotional trend existing throughout a long period in man's history. Though no very specific examples of artwork have come to light before the advent of the Cro-Magnon race, it does not necessarily imply a total lack of art consciousness in the lowlier peoples who preceded them, since relics could readily have been destroyed, or perhaps they have yet to be discovered. There can be no doubt, in fact, that whenever and wherever the artistic spirit occurred in man, it indicated a distinct mental progression over and above anything that he had previously experienced. In all probability the desire to create had lain dormant in his inner consciousness during much of his early development.

Even among the Cro-Magnon peoples, there was a great variety in the quality of the work produced —individual efforts varying according to the skill and proficiency of the artists. Naturally, every scrap and fragment, however poor in execution, is of intense interest to both the anthropologists and artists of the present day. Nevertheless, it will be easily understood that no matter what degree of excellence was attained, the very possession of such an ability confirms once again the presence of the wide gulf separating man's intellectual accomplishments from those of his apelike relatives. It is also of interest to note that, as far as we know, man's earliest approach to art lay in the realistic and *not* in the conventional rendering of his subjects, and that he was busily engaged at such times in depicting just what he saw in the way of animal models of various shapes, sizes, and general characteristics. Though much has been written about the intention of these pictures as a means of propitiating the spirits of the different species represented, we feel that the great majority of them were simply made for the pure delight in producing, as nearly as possible, a record of the living things with which our ancient and primitive ancestors were so well acquainted.

Undoubtedly, in the later stages of their existence, some inklings of the supernatural may have crept into the minds of these splendid men, because of the upward trend of their intellectual capacities during which semireligious beliefs began to lay hold of their deeper emotions. The realization of a difference between beneficent and harmful factors in living conditions, the pinch of hunger and the consequent necessity for securing all the food possible, also contributed largely to the growth of semisuperstitious proclivities so prevalent even now in the present stage of man's development. For some reason, Cro-Magnon man cared very little about immortalizing himself in paint or sculpture, and with the exception of the ponderous female monstrosities already referred to, such subjects are rarely dealt with except in a rather futile way.

Very fortunately, in the cavern of Trois Frères in Southern France, there has been preserved the mural painting of a figure an exception to this latter statement which proves conclusively the presence of a fetish or medicine-man belief in certain Cro-Magnon communities. The image is that of a man with what looks like a horned mask upon his head, a tail, and some kind of furry covering upon his hands. The legs seem painted in stripes of dark color, and the attitude of the figure is both grotesque and sinister in its effect upon a beholder. Here, undoubtedly, is a representation of an early witch doctor or priest, presumably invested with supernatural powers. We can hardly overestimate the cultural value of this priceless relic, replete with all the devilish accoutrements usually associated with his ancient profession, because the figure is evidently no figment of the imagination, being very convincingly human in its minor details. How little its producer could have dreamed that thousands of years after he had gloated quite naturally over the fine results of his handiwork, men not so different from himself would stare at and marvel about the strange horned and tailed figure, so leering and evil-looking, yet still insolently grinning and posturing upon the cavern wall.

It is therefore with a feeling of relief that we turn away from this clever rendering of an ancient charlatan to consider the splendidly executed paintings of bison upon the ceiling of the grotto of Altamira in northern Spain. There can be no occult reason possible for the large colored pictures of a whole herd of these great beasts portrayed in all manner of lifelike positions. Realism of the most evident variety was surely the aim of the man who produced such truly magnificent paintings. Under his magic touch, the rough stone comes to life in a most extraordinary way and one almost hears the fierce, heavily furred brutes bellowing defiance at one another, or resting in very realistic attitudes upon several curious rounded bosses of stone which lie pressed against the ceiling of the cave. The characteristic attitudes of a group of cattle are thoroughly well understood, and the whole effect of the wild, bright-eyed creatures is convincing. Colored chalks of various shades—black, yellow, reddish-brown, and white—are artfully employed in outlining and putting solid color upon these lifelike figures, resulting in a triumph of realistic art by a very keen student of the living form, a true master of his craft even in those early times.

The significant fact that Cro-Magnon man was able and willing to approach the subject of artistic presentation in several different ways merely demonstrates the complicated nature of his inner being. For after all, art in itself is but an outward evidence of some inner workings of the mind, and a desire to express such feelings in a concrete manner. It is therefore one of the most personal of all man's attributes and reflects to a great extent the actual soul yearnings of each individual worker. Undoubtedly, though we are not at the present time able to prove the facts, the curious, deep-seated urge to draw and paint and model was present in the human animal long before the Cro-Magnon race had ever come into being, and their unusual artistic ability was merely a culmination of long ages of wishful thinking and more or less clumsy production by peoples whose history still eludes us. Then too, man's dual nature, partly spiritual, partly animal, gave rise to conflicting ideas regarding the significance of many things and governed to a great extent whatever he was capable of expressing in an artistic manner. A man somewhat mystical or reverential in his thoughts was therefore apt to consider all life including his own as possessing certain magical qualities, traits which he naturally seized upon as appropriate to his particular point of view on life in general. It would be his type undoubtedly who conceived and painted the medicine man just mentioned in our text.

On the other hand, the artist of strictly realistic and highly esthetic tendencies would be deeply impressed by the life vibrations of a great mass of animal forms, such as the bison herd at Altamira. Here it was a task and a pleasure for him to essay the exact reproduction of the grim creatures, so filled with vitality, splendid in form and color and representing very definitely, to his special type of ego, the embodiment of everything that made life worth living. We feel that for the proper understanding of this early art, it is necessary to appreciate the two points of view just described, especially as in all succeeding periods of man's history there will be evidences of similar diversity of conception in the art productions of any given epoch.

Although Cro-Magnon man has proved himself, according to ocular evidence, a very artistic variety of human being, he was at the same time strangely naïve in other ways, though perhaps not so different in personality from his modern representatives. Earthly possessions seem not to have troubled him in the least, and a full stomach, a warm fire, and a place to sleep quite satisfied his physical ambitions. From what strange source he derived his love of art we shall never know, nor why a being so blessed in

some ways should have been so curiously lacking in
a desire for simple comforts of a more material sort.
The plain facts are that apparently he just didn't
care for or feel the need of pottery utensils in which
to keep or cook his food, nor did he know anything
about weaving, or the keeping of domestic animals.
He did manage to clothe himself after a fashion,
using the skins of wild animals as a protection against
the elements, and he sewed these skins together in
some rough manner, because among all the remains
of his weapons and tools we find many well-made
needles of bone and horn. His weapons consisted
principally of barbed bone harpoons or spear points,
and the small flint tools did not amount to much in
his scheme of living. How he was able to kill big
game with the puny spears and darts is still a mystery,
but how the races of men survived at all is a question
of far greater significance and importance. At any
rate, we detect in the history of this splendid race
the flowering of a supreme impulse and one which,
in the centuries to come, was to result in works of
beauty and grandeur far beyond the scope of his
wildest imagination.

Whatever else may be said about the Cro-Magnon
people, they undoubtedly have introduced us to a
phase of man's mentality hitherto not very apparent,
and their lack of practical proclivities is nothing
really detrimental to our admiration for their won-

derful artistic endeavors. Indeed, when next we become acquainted with prehistoric man and his works, most artistic production is distinctly lacking. A long period of time had intervened between the Cro-Magnon man and the races who followed. Living localities, climate, and general environment had changed very definitely. The New, or Polished Stone Age was beginning to show its influence upon the manufactured implements of this new people who undoubtedly had never heard of the artistic Cro-Magnons once so prominent in European prehistory. The origin of these Maglemose tribes is only vaguely understood, but we know that they dwelt along the Baltic coast of Europe, and that they were industrious, clever, and far more versatile than the Cro-Magnons. Art, however, meant little to them, and their entire lives were involved in practical living. They made no pottery, and polished well-made implements of bone, fashioned boats from hollowed logs, possibly had a simple form of loom, practiced farming, and fished with nets and hooks. Naturally fishing played a prominent part in their social existence. But under such prosaic conditions, we suspect that the brilliantly artistic renderings of animal life accomplished by the Cro-Magnons were now a thing of the past.

When evidences of resurgent art again appeared, the realistic approach was decidedly absent, though we can observe faint glimmerings of a type of conventional drawing, primarily intended as a decoration either upon pieces of pottery or on clothing and ornaments for the human form. The artistic spirit did not succumb readily in man's mental processes though it suffered serious lapses from time to time for reasons which we can only conjecture. The phenomenon of its rejuvenation is equally obscure, because there never was an absolute necessity for art in the lives of any people. Its persistent recurrence is therefore a sign of a deep-seated origin in man's inner being, coincident with the mental and spiritual side of his development away from his early mammalian ancestors. Indeed, man's history without the leaven of this superimaginative asset would be but a sorry affair, a chronicle of advancement, to be sure, but lacking the romance and profound mental stimulus so typical of the human species. In dealing with a creature as complicated intellectually as ourselves, the delicate impressions of every kind that constantly influence the mind must all be clearly appreciated. Some of these will necessarily be much deeper than others, and will have a correspondingly strong effect upon our thoughts and actions.

It would seem that between the advent and the departure of Cro-Magnon man (a period of thousands of years) certain basic traits of the truly human side of our cosmos had become firmly established. The earlier and more bestial characteristics of the mammal known as *Homo sapiens* were to be relegated to the background of our consciousness and held in abeyance by the dominating force of our higher ambitions. The need for some continuing form of art expression fortunately proved to be one of these many attainments, varying widely from age to age in its application as new objects of man's useful handiwork, or his highly improved and more complicated weapons, gave fresh opportunities for embellishment along esthetic lines. In other words, because the underlying desire for some sort of beautification of things around him was still innate, early man was to branch out artistically into many new forms and methods of applying pleasing lines and colors and forms to a host of different subjects. The gradual change from chipped flint weapons and implements to better and more elegant polished stone objects with which to carry on his various activities was a forward step in this direction, and once started it gave rise to a whole new series of hatchets, spear and arrow points, and household tools of many kinds. The hatchet head, once merely fastened by thongs to its handle, was drilled through expertly in such a way that the handle was inserted into the orifice thus created, and as a consequence the efficiency of the weapon was much enhanced. It was found, also,

Cliffs of the Font-de-Gaume cavern where examples of Cro-Magnon art may still be seen

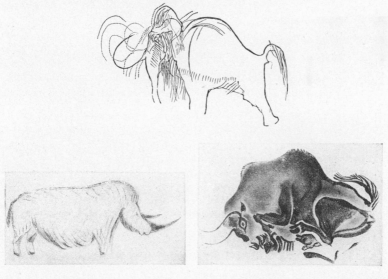

Three drawings considered among the best produced by Cro-Magnon artists

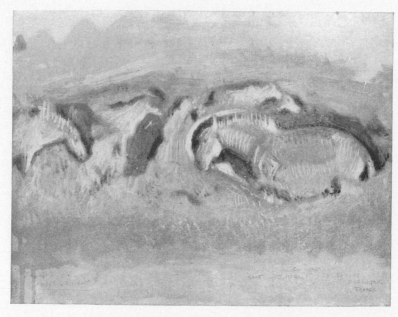

Frieze of sculptured horses at Cap-Blanc

Przewalski horses painted from life

that a polished edge could be given to the hitherto
chipped edge of the stone axe, thereby making the
cutting part very much keener.

A Stone Age Dolmen

Not content, however, with merely perfecting the
practical phase of all such useful objects, the curiously artistic mind of man was forever learning to
appreciate the finer shapes, curves, and proportions
of the things his skillful hands were able to create.
More elegant objects stirred something in his
make-up as he continued to advance mentally and
mystically through the passing ages. The rite of
burial, practiced even in early days, began to assume
much greater significance in his daily existence, and
gave a decided impetus to his constructive talents,
a branch of art hitherto confined to the simplest of
building formations. No longer content with a simple
burial in the earth and the placing of chaplets of
stones and shells about the head of the departed, our
fast-developing ancestors gave vent to their reverential feelings by creating more and more elaborate
burial places, constructing them of stones or making

mounds of earth in which the body was placed after certain primitive ceremonies had been completed.

A Bell Barrow

It is quite apparent, as we study all these different manifestations, that the complex beings from which we ourselves have descended were determined not only to perpetuate themselves while living, by the usual natural processes, but that they were equally set upon a system whereby the body would continue to function after death. With this latter idea constantly growing in the consciousness of the human race, we are not surprised to note the growing importance attached to funeral rites and ceremonies throughout all the realm of prehistoric man. As a consequence of these more or less spiritually conceived notions, a much enhanced reverence for the dead becomes apparent in the care with which all functions pertaining to burial customs were conducted. Nothing was too good for the souls of the departed, and the most elaborate weapons and ornaments among the tribal possessions were reverentially placed near the form of a relative or clan chief at the time of an interment. We refer to these customs here because their existence must have been of vast importance in the purely artistic history of the various races of men who succeeded each other through thousands of years of this early development.

No résumé of prehistoric art would be complete without a comprehension of this early association of semireligious and artistic ideas in the developing human mind and a realization of the powerful impetus to superior artistic achievement which such association created. The strangely susceptible mind of a human being is readily influenced by any thoughts of an existence beyond the grave because of the all-pervading egoistic yearnings of his inner being. He doesn't want to die, but if he has to do so, then every precaution should be taken whereby he may later continue his interrupted existence in some new and more congenial sphere. Such conception is a very ancient one in man's mentality and began perhaps, though in a vague and ephemeral way, soon after he had slipped away from his earthier connections with his primate relatives. Again in Neanderthal days, a similar notion must have entered his none too well developed consciousness, because even those crude individuals took trouble about the comfort of their defunct relations in order to protect them from destruction by wild animals. Primitive as was this idea, it disclosed the presence of a wish for an immortality which asserted itself in the mind of a very early savage. This being so, we shall not be able to divorce the prosaic from the mystical and religious in man's history, but on the contrary the tremendous results which the latter conception has effected will become more evident, not only in their influence upon his whole mode of social existence, but also upon the artistic side of his nature.

Naturally, under these conditions the skill of the artistic members of the community was in constant demand, and we become aware of an ever-growing tendency to decorate with all the accumulated cleverness of the ages, not only objects connected with mystical rites, but also the homelier appurtenances of an everyday existence. In this comparatively recent period in man's history, such practical equipment had increased tremendously both in number and in the variety of materials utilized in it's manufacture. It is a far cry from the very remote periods of our existence when only the simplest of weapons and tools were conceived within the very restricted limitations of a more primitive mentality. At the time of which we are now speaking, some ten to twenty thousand years ago, both the temporal and the growing spiritual mentality of man had assumed such complicated proportions that the scope for artistic activities was fast gaining a position of outstanding importance in human economy. The decoration of burial places, implements and dwelling huts, pottery, weapons, and jewelry offered unlimited scope for the demonstration of artistic talent, while the variety of materials with which to work was soon to be augmented by the discovery of bronze as a splendid new medium of great significance to the human race in general. When, how, and where this wonderful alloy was first utilized is a matter of pure speculation, but we know that it does not appear among the possessions of early man until toward the close of the Polished Stone Age. As bronze is a metal resulting from the combination of copper and tin, its first production must have been a purely accidental one. Pure copper probably had been known and its remarkable qualities recognized long before some quick-witted artisan had perhaps stumbled upon the fact that the fusing under heat of the two metals would, when cold and pounded with a stone hammer, make a totally new and highly useful material for the production of an endless assortment of practical and ornamental objects.

We may picture to ourselves the satisfaction of that great and momentous event, far greater in fact than the interested workers could ever have imagined. Whatever the circumstances connected with this unique accomplishment, the bright, hard metal soon usurped the use of stone and bone as a medium for the manufacture of objects, particularly when the technique of casting it in sand molds was perfected. Here again, we are at a loss to explain the amazing significance of that discovery, especially when one considers the various processes required for its successful production. We can imagine that an inquisitive worker, intensely interested in his newly found combination of tin and copper, might easily have dropped some of the fiery liquid into a hole in sandy ground, and observed with amazement how perfectly the soft metal assumed the irregular shape of the depression. Alert and curious, he might have tried the feat again by scraping the definite forms of a dagger or sword blade in the sharp gritty sand, and experienced the extreme delight of seeing the molten bronze assume that same form when poured into the depression. How cleverly these old-time craftsmen profited by the knowledge thus gained we can see today in any collection of prehistoric weapons. In fact, the advent of bronze in man's economic existence proved to be a milestone of cultural advancement of the very highest order.

Although well aware of all these advantages, man, being a creature of habit, was in no hurry to completely abandon his former flint and bone weapons and utensils. We find them often in the very same deposits which contain the bronze objects. While the first molding of bronze was probably achieved by the method just described, it was not long before ancient man conceived the idea of making two molds, either in stone or sand, which when fitted together left a hollow space the shape of the desired object. Into this space the liquid bronze was poured and allowed to cool and harden. It was a simple technique to remove the two sides of the mold disclosing the now perfected shape of a sword or spear point in all its bright beauty. The finishing was only a matter of polishing with sand and water until exactly the proper form was attained. The astonishing skill and proficiency displayed by these early founders is a matter of no small wonder to the present-day anthropologist, who can but marvel as he gazes upon most artistically shaped weapons, bowls, jewelry of every sort, pots and chains, fishhooks, sickles, horns and other musical instruments.

Celtic Cinerary Urns

Naturally these accomplishments did not materialize at once in man's economy. As usual it took time and experience to improve upon his first lowly experiments with the wonderful metallic substance.

Still, as always, advancement for man seemed inevitable. His restless, inventive, and highly intelligent mind could conceive of nothing but improvement and alteration in the form and manufacture of whatever he chose to fashion with his skillful fingers, guided by the superior quality of his inner motivation. Since, at the time, his dwellings, boats, and clothing were still in the primitive stage, the artistic urge was naturally centered upon his weapons and home utensils, and the decoration of his person with all sorts of adornment calculated to impart luster to his ever-increasing ego. In bronze he had found the ideal substance for the carrying out of all such esthetic ideas, and he proceeded to demonstrate prowess in that direction to a really remarkable degree. Swords and daggers and spearpoints became real works of art under this inspiration, and he learned to chase and cast in relief upon urns and jars and pots all manner of interesting and beautiful things, treated more or less conventionally but none the less successfully. Figures of animals and men, mystical signs and writings of a sort, processions of people, trees, and flowers, shells and other desirable and revered objects were presented in a multitude of fascinating conceptions expertly executed and indicative of the tremendous forward strides in culture then spreading over large sections of the inhabited world. What knowledge our old-time relatives were acquiring in the construction of dwellings, boats, and tombs for the dead, and the decorations and high degree of artistic skill demonstrated in these activities, we can learn from a study of the many known examples of this ancient work. When in succeeding periods the manufacture of iron objects became a part of man's culture, a whole new line of opportunities manifested itself. And the wonderfully hard and resistant properties of the new metal again enhanced his manufacturing abilities in scores of ways.

Beehive Hut

Art and industry went merrily forward in those distant days, each inseparable from the other, a truly ideal and desirable condition from every point of view. But, if we stop a moment to ponder over the whole matter, man's peculiar attribute—the esthetic part of his being— and the causes for his having been so prompted, will remain as remote and inexplicable as ever. For no practical reason exists which necessitates such a display of inner feeling. Everything ever made might just as well have been left without a single mark or line or decorative motif imposed upon its general shape or surface. This curious desire to make marks was, however, apparently one of his earlier proclivities and he might have loved to draw and model in the primal stages of his history. However that may be, he certainly has distinguished himself mightily in the later days of his development and stands forth the greatest and finest builder the world has ever seen as well as the artistic genius of all creation. The difficulty of describing even casually the number, scope, and scale of his later artistic activities is evidently quite impossible in a book of this type, but we can call attention to the titanic proportions of his great building attempts prompted as they were by semireligious motives, and carried out with great skill and an immense amount of labor. At the same time his boats —at first merely rafts or roughed-out logs—began to be fashioned more elaborately with an eye to graceful and beautiful proportions. Both the bow and stern posts served as focal points for decorative and often symbolical embellishment, and the hull of the vessel was carefully shaped as well for speed and water resistance. The built-up craft soon took the place of the hollowed single log, and its size increased accordingly. No longer was early man confined to terra

Boat from Bronze Age (Denmark)

firma. With the new techniques he constructed quite sizable vessels, able to travel through rough water and propelled by hardy oarsmen for whom the sea apparently had few terrors. In no one branch of endeavor was man's artistry more evident than in the making of these sturdy sea-going little ships, accurately constructed with fine lines and stalwart frames, well proportioned and adequately designed for their strenuous existence in a treacherous and powerful element. The early artist really came into his own in the elaborate painting and carving lavished upon these most useful examples of man's handiwork, and the art of a people was frequently well exemplified in such construction and ornamentation.

At the time of which we are speaking, wood was naturally the sole material employed in the building of a vessel, and this custom continued for thousands of years even up to our own day and time. It is difficult to imagine the race without a means of traveling upon the water so that in ancient times as now the lure of the sea developed into a persistent passion among those sections of humanity living along the shore line of every great continent. Always a creature of a complex mentality, man turned hither and yon to improve himself and his living conditions in general. While he developed scores of diverse interests, conceiving them to be either necessary or adding to his comfort and convenience, he was resourceful and

immensely versatile and he learned to experiment
and make himself proficient in many mediums.
Though he recognized in bronze a splendid substance
for the casting of his numerous pots, urns, and vases,
and its possibility as a superior decorative medium,
at the same time the Bronze Age man did not over-
look the fact that his crockery and unglazed clay
forms were also suitably and carefully painted and
incised with all sorts of interesting and tasteful
patterns.

Celtic Vase from the Bronze Age

In the art of weaving, at which he also excelled,
the loom and its products played a large part in the
social and domestic life of the community. Cloth with
appropriate designs and even colors soon became a
very necessary part of the family belongings. Indeed
one of the most interesting phases in man's history
is the astonishing number and variety of his achievements in the material sense, once the full measure
of his human mentality had been attained. To his

newly awakened capabilities, nothing seemed too complicated or too difficult, while the scope of varied artistic productions apparently kept pace with every new invention.

Strangely enough, in spite of the long series of decorated objects of every description, we do not again see until Egyptian times any attempt at the realistic renderings of animals once so beautifully portrayed by the Cro-Magnon cave artists. Either the late Stone and Bronze and Iron Age men were too busy and too engrossed in the mere problems of living, or perhaps their very outlook upon the entire subject had undergone a drastic change. There are apparently periods in man's development when certain phases of his many-sided mentality are in the ascendant, when art, for example, assumes a paramount position in the scheme of life. At such times, we are treated to a revelation of what the human race can actually accomplish along esthetic lines, if their minds are focused in that direction. These successive waves of art inspiration have exhibited many forms and fluctuations over long periods of time, and with widely varied results. It would not be here appropriate to discuss man's superb artistic work in a day subsequent to the birth of the historical record of his achievement. However, it is hoped that we have made a trifle clearer those early efforts of our forefathers which lay within the artistic field of human

experience, as well as the motivating influences behind those efforts. The desire to express something
outside the humdrum monotony of their precarious
situation, some inner yearnings and hidden repres-
sions to be recorded, may account for many of his
artistic efforts, but the larger and more profound
reasons for any such form of mental activity may
well forever remain a mystery.

ANIMAL LIFE IN PREHISTORY

In all our studies of prehistoric man, his feeble
beginnings and subsequent evolution, we are impressed with the fact that his development was always associated with the animal life of the time, so
that whether in the warm and humid depths of a
tropical forest, the open glades of a savannah
country or the damp and inhospitable caves and
rock shelters of a northern habitat, there was in-
variably present a coexistent fauna. In the steaming
murky jungles of Asia and its islands lurked great
flesh-eating saber-toothed tigers, deadly foes of the
Pithecanthropus family, while elephants, hippopotamus, buffaloes, and other fearsome brutes could beat
down and trample the fragile dwelling places of
primitive ape men. In Africa, where both open
plains and forested country gave refuge to our still

earlier relatives such as *Plesianthropus*, there were other types of mammals to be reckoned with—antelopes, hyenas, probably some lionlike carnivora, and troops of fierce and agile baboons, the last being terribly cunning and ferocious brutes when attacked or disturbed. In the cold and partly glaciated regions of western Europe were living at different periods whole groups of widely divergent mammalian stocks: horses, bears, oxen, deer, rhinoceros, elephants, lions, hyenas, bison, and a host of smaller creatures—foxes, wolves, lemmings, hamsters, etc.—too numerous to mention.

All this tremendous aggregation of animal life was profoundly influenced by climatic and geographical variations as these fundamental conditions changed under drastic and even revolutionary influences of worldwide scope and power. Oceans altered their level, either rising to new heights and submerging great areas of former dry land or sinking away and exposing whole regions formerly at the bottom of the sea. Again, mountain chains rising far into the atmosphere created gigantic cloud masses and air currents of the first magnitude, and volcanic action with its resulting outbursts of lava and ashes often annihilated entire regions, killing off completely all forms of animal life including man himself in the great catastrophe. Most terrible and far-reaching in lethal effects, however, was the succession of glacial and interglacial periods which for hundreds of thousands of years of man's existence alternately warmed and froze vast sections of the earth's surface, especially in the northern hemisphere. All living things felt the power and resistless force of these mighty climatic upsets, and the animals and plants of any given region were in a constant state of change and geographic distribution as they strove to accommodate themselves to new land and water levels and profound vacillations of temperature and humidity.

Naturally under such conditions man as an animal suffered much and perhaps became practically exterminated at times in certain parts of his environment. Often he and the animal life about him were forced to abandon for ages great land areas which had once been a salubrious dwelling place for thousands of living creatures. In the matter of protection against cold he was by nature a sadly deficient being because his body, while possibly more hirsute than at present, never apparently possessed to a marked degree the ability to grow a long, thick overcoat of fur and hair against the rigors of a severely cold climate. As a result, in certain regions he was obliged to spend at least a part of his days in killing all sorts of animals whose warm, furry skins might later be used to cover his shivering, naked form. But the difficulties encountered in attacking and disposing of these tremendously powerful game animals called for courage and resourcefulness of a high order, and the types of animals which even the poorly armed Neanderthals were able to dispose of have always astonished anthropologists. One must remember, however, that while the great brutes encountered were far superior in strength to their human adversaries, they were also distinctly inferior in mental acumen and sagacity. Man's superintelligence has ever been his one extraordinary asset, even in the early days of emergence from the anthropoid level of mentality.

The effect of climate on the animal life of our world is not too well appreciated by the casual reader, who merely accepts as a fact the great differences in the species inhabiting various sections of the planet's surface. Naturally our forebears were in a condition of absolute ignorance on this point, nor as a matter of fact could such information have been of the slightest value to them in their daily living regime. Certainly an austere realism prevailed in the good old days of man's infancy and adolescence because life was hard and often terribly dangerous, and his means of defense and offense were of the poorest and weakest variety. But we of a later time who essay to follow with intensity life's ancient story are able to draw inferences from the continuous and changing successions of plants and animals which are retrieved as fossils in all parts of the world.

We know, for example, that the presence of tropical fauna and flora which existed in Europe before the first glaciation, perhaps 500,000 years ago, was surely indicative of a warm climate. The figures tell with a modicum of accuracy the beginning of what geologists know as the glacial periods of the northern hemisphere. Not to be too technical, there were four of these icy invasions combined with those interglacial eras during which prevailing temperatures and general conditions became more suitable for all plant or animal forms and species. While to the layman 500,000 years seem a tremendously long time, to the professional it counts as but yesterday in the stupendous ages of world history. Indeed, so recent is this period that with comparatively few exceptions the faunal and floral life of the world has changed very little in its general aspect during that time. To be sure, there were several important mammals which are now extinct such as the woolly mammoth, woolly rhinoceros, saber-toothed tiger, cave bear and others. But in the main both plants and animals show a surprisingly tenacious resistance to obliteration after weathering for a half million years what was probably the greatest series of climatic revolutions in the later periods of world history.

This seeming tenacity however, this hanging on to life in spite of environmental changes, was only possible because of the vast adaptability of many of the species involved. Thus, while the mild climate

of preglacial time was favorable to the approach of
warm-country creatures from the east and south in
Africa and Asia, when more severe conditions began
to prevail these same animals may have acquired
thicker coats of hair, and become gradually accustomed to lower temperatures and sterner living conditions generally. In this way, the presence of
hippopotamus, southern elephants, mammoths, rhinoceros, antelopes, hyenas, and other warm country
species may be accounted for satisfactorily.

But when weather conditions grew intensely severe
in northern Europe and the great glaciers began to
roll down the long mountain slopes and the snow
lay in huge drifts in the valleys, even such vast and
heavily furred beasts as the woolly mammoth, the
musk ox, the reindeer, and the woolly rhinoceros
were obliged to retreat before the rigors of a too
glacial milieu and betook themselves to the more
southern regions of Europe, where they were apparently able to survive in vast numbers with the abundant food supply and a winter climate of only
moderate severity.

Anatomically, as already stated, man's teeth did
not indicate the eating of flesh as part of his diet
except perhaps in negligible quantities. Yet his history will show that for some reason he was always
essentially a meat eater by opportunity. Even the
lowly *Plesianthropus* of South Africa may have

feasted on the baboons in his immediate vicinity. Some credence can be placed in this idea because of the singular holes which pierce the skulls of so many of these formidible creatures in the *Plesianthropus* beds at Sterkfontein in South Africa. These holes were certainly not made by the teeth of any animal, but were inflicted by some clumsily pointed weapon in the hands of a being who knew how to wield it. No great ape would kill an adversary in any such manner, which leaves us wondering whether *Plesianthropus* himself might not have been the guilty party. It is pure conjecture, of course, thus to ascribe the clever killing instinct to so lowly a being, but the urge to destroy, present even in the great apes, was doubly intensified in primitive man. Whether at that distant day he devoured what he had killed is possible, but not entirely probable.

In the ages to come, however, man was certainly to assume the role of prime destroyer, and his flesh-eating propensities kept pace with his increasingly phenomenal ability to manufacture weapons both for offense and defense. He was always obliged to live "off the country," which in his case was a decidedly limited section of the local landscape, having no better means of getting about than his own two legs. There were animals all about him no matter what part of the world he inhabited, though naturally the species varied according to locality. Some of these he was able to kill without too much trouble and danger to himself; others of the carnivorous persuasion were constantly on the alert to kill *him* whenever they had the opportunity. So it was that our ancestors existed always in an uncertain state of being, either playing the role of destroyer or being destroyed themselves.

THE CAVE BEAR

There were certain of his enemies, however, which figured very largely and for long ages in the European sections of his habitat. Chief among these we may cite the great cave bear, *Ursus spelaeus,* a huge species with an enormous head, powerful talons, and a most unpleasant habit of occupying caves which might otherwise have served as shelter for exhausted men, especially when winter storms roared across the land, and deep snow and bitter cold made living in the open well nigh impossible. From the numerous remains of these massive creatures (800 skeletons being unearthed in one single grotto in France), we are able to judge of their numbers during long periods of the Glacial epoch. They were tenacious and menacing brutes from any standpoint, possessing tremendous strength and a certain cunning which made them dangerous and terrible adversaries. When one considers the puny weapons used by such races as the Neanderthal peoples, the wonder is that they were able to kill these formidable animals even though several hunters were engaged in the fray. The employment of dogs in the chase was a thing quite unknown in their day simply because the dog as such had never then been domesticated. So that it was a case of man kill bear, or vice-versa, whenever these doughty antagonists met in mortal combat.

Armed as is modern man with high-powered and deadly rifles, the killing of an animal, no matter how big or fierce, is merely child's play compared to the violent and protracted duels in which ancestral man was often the central figure. From what we can glean by a study of the cave bear's skeleton, he was a very large animal, perhaps weighing twelve or fifteen hundred pounds, with sharp teeth, terrible claws, and a fighting heart. In character he very closely resembled the more recent European brown bear, *Ursus arctos,* but was altogether larger and therefore a force to be reckoned with. When attacked he no doubt stood erect as does his modern counterpart, and with arms extended, mouth open, and claws ready for action, his general appearance was formidable in the extreme. Bears, at least all the species known to us, are tough and determined adversaries. They never give up and they never stop fighting until death overtakes them. Our own grizzlies and Kodiak bears, as well as the Polar species, have long been celebrated for their do-or-die qualities when cornered or wounded, and undoubtedly these characteristics were equally a part of the cave bear's psychology.

It is fair to assume that no other animal contemporaneous with these huge creatures could best them in a fight, that is no animal other than man, the most expert and dangerous slayer the world has ever known. Small and physically weak compared to their enormous physique, he nevertheless by dint of an extraordinary courage, resourcefulness, and downright savage brutality could and did overcome these ponderous creatures on many occasions. It wasn't always a fair fight because we have reason to believe that many of the big animals were destroyed by the smoking-out process—a method in which a great fire built at the mouth of some ursine retreat would gradually produce such a volume of smoke within the cave shelter that the unfortunate inmates would stumble out of the entrance in a more or less asphyxiated condition. There, ranged on either side by ferocious Neanderthalers armed with spears, clubs, rocks, and other deadly missiles, they were clubbed, struck on the head with heavy stone hatchets, or transfixed by sharply pointed spears. Undoubtedly, many escaped and when the battle was over, these ferocious little men salved their own wounds and carried off some member of the tribe whose head had been smashed by a fierce blow from the paw of an enraged bear.

Such trifles attended to, the brave fellows set to work with their flint knives and roughly chipped coups-de-poing or hand hatchets, flaying the great carcasses and tearing off the reeking hides from the huge and muscular bodies. Cast aside for the moment, the skins were later dried and then perhaps crudely tanned to make them again flexible.

The women often took part in these proceedings, for it was their role in the household economy to fashion the furry pelts, cutting and shaping them into some sort of crude garment against the cold of a glacial winter. We have no means of knowing whether man ate the flesh of the cave bear, but the chances are strongly in favor of it. Our ancestors could not afford to be finicky in their diet, being always but a few steps ahead of starvation, and the meat of the great animal, especially when roasted over a hot fire, no doubt was excellent and nutritious provender for hungry savages.

THE LEOPARD

The nightly chore of locking doors and shutting windows bothered our ancient relatives not at all, since caves and rock shelters weren't fitted with such annoying equipment. On the contrary, our ancestors were painfully exposed to all sorts of outside influences, many of a most baleful character. One never knew on retiring whether one would actually be there when morning broke. For whatever the conditions under which our race existed for ages, security was not one of them. Prowling beasts of various types were always abroad during the hours of darkness, seeking their prey wherever it was to be found. What man did to save himself before he discovered the use of fire is impossible to say, and even this method of protection was not always successful. There have been numerous cases even in recent times when men sleeping about a campfire in the open or even within the shelter of a tent or hut have been seized by a prowling leopard or hyena, and either killed or terribly injured before they could be rescued.

The remains of leopardlike carnivora are not commonly found fossil in European bone deposits, but those of the saber-tooths, and later the lion are frequently exhumed, especially in caves. As is the case today, the presence of great numbers of herbivorous animals—horses, cattle, sheep, goats, or deer and antelope—surely acted as a lodestone to the flesh eaters of the region. Although we do not as a rule realize the fact, of the two great types of mammalian life, carnivora and herbivora, the former is dependent upon the latter for his livelihood on the principle that with no flesh to eat, no flesh eater remains in existence. It doesn't work this way at all when the sequence is reversed, for under the relief from persecution and destruction by flesh eaters, the timid deer, antelopes, and sheep and cattle often multiply beyond all conscience, to a point where they may even destroy themselves by consuming all the green things in places where they are too abundant. Such catastrophes must have been practically unknown in prehistoric days when men were few in the world and their most destructive tactics left untouched vast areas of feeding grounds for countless herds of big game, always with their accompanying satellites—wolves, bears, lions, leopards, and hyenas.

Today the lion and leopard are confined to the continents of Asia and Africa, but in the glacial periods the huge cave lions, in Europe at any rate, were able to grow coats of dense fur and hair much as do the Siberian tigers of the present day. Leopards, as well, donned their heavy layers of fur as the winter advanced in their chosen habitats. They were always hungry, cunning, audacious, and exceedingly active animals, much smaller but no less formidable than a lion, and their size and protectively spotted coats (presuming they were so decorated at the time) rendered them practically invisible to the sharp eyes of a wandering cave man.

The dozing savage in the picture on page 112 nods as he sits before his little fire, his wife and baby sleeping unconcernedly in their shallow rock shelter.

The cunning beast above them is naturally afraid of the bright glow of the embers, but hunger will do much to bolster the courage of such a fierce and dangerous animal, and the guardian of the cavern sleeps fitfully, worn out with the constant struggle against conditions in general. Perhaps a flashing yellow body will fall swiftly upon the helpless watcher and carry away the unfortunate man before the wakened woman can come to his assistance. On the stage of man's early existence such tragedies were commonplace, simply a natural episode which might occur at any moment in his short earthly career. There is nothing unusual in this ghastly occurrence because it all seems a part of some strictly natural series of events. Man and his animal contemporaries came and went through long ages, some types vanishing entirely, others maintaining themselves in spite of everything that nature could do to hurry them into oblivion.

THE WOOLLY RHINOCEROS AND MAMMOTH

Reference should be made to a spirited and quite accurate wall painting of the woolly rhinoceros, *Tichorhinus*. This is the creature mentioned in the chapter on cave exploration which was set off by itself in the far recesses of the Font de Gaume grotto

at Les Eyzies in Southern France. Other drawings
of this wonderful animal occur in several caverns of
prehistoric art, but none can be compared to this
particular painting in brilliance of execution. It
accurately depicts several important points in the
peculiar profile of this singular pachyderm. We are
struck at once by the representation of long hair
which apparently covered the animal from head to
tail. This unique appearance immediately sets off the
woolly rhinoceros from any living species and may
indeed even in his own day have been one of his
outstanding characteristics. The upper lip was evidently pointed in the manner of the modern black
rhinoceros of Africa, and the ears and tail were
small, as befitted a denizen of a cold climate. The
body was long and the legs short, with a peculiar
hump or protuberance just at the back of the skull
upon the short, thick neck. Were we not accustomed
to this unusual feature by noting the same form in
the white rhinoceros, an African species of the present time, it might be a matter of curiosity not easily
explained. As a matter of fact, the hump is a fleshy
bulge of tough and sinewy texture, the great neck
ligament which, when the creature's head is raised,
seems to buckle into a kind of contracted knot of
flesh and tendon. Two long horns somewhat like
those of its modern white relative projected forward,
one from the forehead, the other from the top of

the nose. So clearly are all these features indicated in the beautiful drawing that they leave no room for speculation as to just what the artist saw before him in the days when actual living rhinoceros fed and fought and rushed about in the cold and rigorous climate of the last glaciation in Southern France. This chilly region was by no means the only home of the fierce woolly creature, because his habitat extended over many other parts of the globe during the long cooling-off period which prevailed at the close of the Old Stone Age.

We are most fortunate also in having actual specimens of this animal in the flesh, as examples have been unearthed in various parts of Europe. Several years ago in Starunia in Eastern Galicia, one was found buried at a depth of thirty feet and in a fairly complete state of preservation. The body and head covered with hair of a golden color over a skin coat of wool showed plainly the appearance in life of this remarkable animal. The find proves how accurately the Cro-Magnon artist had observed his contemporaneous model and indicated all the characteristic features.

The constant association of the woolly mammoth and the double-horned pachyderm is evidenced by the finding of their remains usually in close proximity, or intermingled. Naturally they must have wandered about their ancient grazing area together, resting and generally living in amity throughout the course of a long existence. How strange they must have appeared to the Cro-Magnon observers, these two huge hairy beasts much the same in color but so different in general contour! The mammoth with his vastly greater bulk and huge tusks loomed high above the squat but powerful and grotesque form of his double-horned companion. A curious pair, indeed, each tolerating the presence of the other, but similarly afraid and suspicious of their archenemy, man.

For man, it seems, was the black sheep of all that vast aggregation of animal life which roamed many parts of the world in interglacial times. No creatures trusted this insignificant, but dangerous little object whose appearance so often spread death and destruction in their midst. They could not understand yet altogether feared the sharp spear thrust, the terrific blows of a heavy club, and the flaming torches held high above the heads of these ferocious two-legged beings. Whenever such a battle occurred, it meant a fight to the death, and the equally savage rhinoceros was often the victor in these titanic struggles. At such a time, the hunter caught off guard was hurled into the air by an upward toss of the great horned head and falling, was either trampled or gored to death by the infuriated animal. Might against ingenuity was the watchword of the day as it long had been in man's tremendous efforts to maintain himself under the varying conditions of his local environment. In any case, his descendants have survived to populate the earth, while all that is left of the woolly rhinoceros are scattered bones and teeth, and an occasional mummified remnant of a once magnificent and formidable creature.

Since the woolly mammoth and the woolly rhinoceros have been mentioned as apparently inseparable companions, it is appropriate to describe the former animal just here in the text. Our knowledge of this great creature is much more complete than is the case with most extinct animals. Like the woolly rhinoceros, it has been found frozen in the ice in an almost perfect condition. Indeed, in some cases practically the entire body of the animal has come to light after the lapse of many centuries. Such an instance occurred in Siberia some years ago when after a warm spell of weather and the consequent melting of the ice sheet, the tremendous and fearsome form of some great animal became visible to the local peasantry. The authorities at St. Petersburg, hearing of this discovery, dispatched experts to the scene and much of the vast creature, hair, flesh, and all were retrieved and finally deposited in the museum of the Russian metropolis. Modern man viewed for the first time the bones and flesh and tusks of the great woolly mammoth, a species of fossil elephant found not only in Europe and Asia, but also on the

Cro-Magnon artist at work

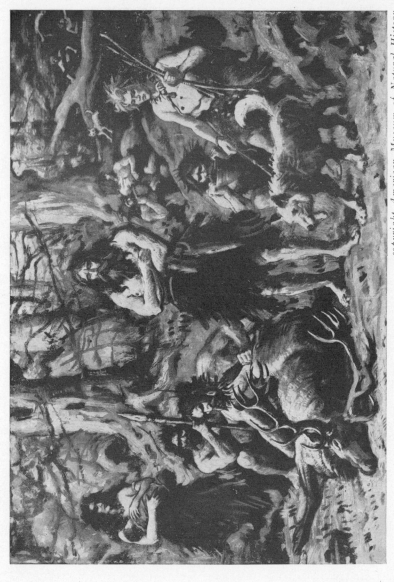

The death of a red stag during the Polished Stone Age

North American continent. Since that day, other specimens have been freed from their covering of frozen gravel and ice and mud, and variously acquired, treated, and prepared by scientists in many countries. The dense hairy and woolly covering of the great *Proboscidean* is evidence of a life passed under extremely frigid climatic conditions.

To our ancestors as well as to ourselves, the impressive size, color, form, and truly extraordinary appearance of the massive brute strikes an almost reverential chord in the human heart. A sense of grandeur and dignity emanates from such an imperial presence made doubly striking by the masses of hair which drape the huge creature in a dark auburn garment of cold-resisting insulation. For here without exception, in the author's opinion, is the quintessence of mammalian body development—the finest, largest, and with the exception of man and the higher primates, the most intelligent of all animals. No wonder then that we see in prehistoric art so many representations of the titanic pachyderm, or that its bones are so often discovered about the camps and shelters of our early ancestors. Mammoth flesh when cut from a young animal must have been tasty and satisfying to a horde of gaunt savages who with gleeful shouts proceeded to crack every long bone for the marrow it contained, while they gorged themselves on the bulky remains of some unfortunate tusker which had either been killed while mired in a swamp or else clubbed to death as it lay helpless at the bottom of some deep and artfully constructed pitfall.

It must be remembered that the woolly mammoth represented only a single species of fossil elephant, a branch of the great proboscidean stock which had originated in a presumably warm climate, and that it was the northern form of a long series of early elephants which had been developing for hundreds of thousands of years in Asia and Africa. In earlier European history, in the warmer periods before the great glacial eras, there were several species of mammothlike proportions which roamed as far north as the British Isles. These were huge animals, but probably not covered with the protecting cover of long coarse hair.

Why the woolly variety elected to exist in the inhospitable climate of glacial Europe is naturally a mystery, but it was apparently able to withstand the rigors of that period for thousands of years. In the course of time, as is the case with everything else in nature, the hand of fate weighed heavily upon many animal species. Mammoths, woolly rhinoceros, cave bears, even Cro-Magnon man himself succumbed to the archdestroyer. Perhaps the climate grew too severe for these spartan inhabitants of the country; or pestilence, famine, or fire may have so depleted the stocks that all finally perished. The mammoths, owing to their extraordinary powers of resistance, might well have been the last to give up the struggle for existence waged against we know not what odds.

One can imagine how in the depths of some terrible winter, with bushes and grasses covered deep in snow, the destruction of the great herds was finally accomplished. Gales and bitter cold perhaps first decimated the younger and weaker members of the groups, and the fate of even the strongest individuals became at length an assured fact under the pressure of months of starvation. Each morning saw many of the beaten creatures lying dead or exhausted in the huge drifts until only the patriarchs of the once great clans remained alive. With waving trunks and feeble trumpetings they greeted the coming day, but at length even their huge frames began to weaken. In the wan sunlight of early spring great mounds of white slowly melted above the prostrate forms, the pale gleam from ivory tusks like smooth curved headstones marking the resting place of this superb race of mammalian giants now forever passed into the limbo of vanished things.

THE URUS (*Bos primigenius*)

The horned cattle (the *Bovidae* of science) are a comparatively recent development in the history of evolution. This means that their existence here, which yet is a matter of many thousands of years, is dwarfed by comparison with the vastly greater length of the age of mammals in general, a period of perhaps 50,000,000 years. There were apparently two or three great stocks of so-called bison, represented today by our own species and the remnants of the European form, as well as the buffaloes of Africa and India, and the zebus, gaurs, and banting species of the Far East. The musk ox, once an apparently common animal in Europe, is now confined to Greenland and the northern part of our continent. The great wild ox, companion of so many now extinct European mammals, is itself no longer in existence, though reported in certain sections of that continent until the past three or four hundred years. Caesar mentions it in his treatise, yet in Roman times the domesticated strains were evidently not members of this great wild type, but probably came from the east.

Bos primigenius was an animal of imposing mien, long-legged, long-horned, and very quick and powerful in its movements. There is a marked resemblance between the cave drawings of this splendid creature and the old time "long horns" of our great southwest, whose ancestors were brought here by the early Spanish conquerors. It is said that the likeness is only superficial, but one can not help thinking that there might be some distant connection between the two strains. Whatever truth there may be in that statement, the line is not at all distinct, nor can it be proved by any historical references as to its accuracy. Prehistoric man was not, we must remember, impressed by fancied relationships in the animals he hunted for food. On the contrary, his one idea was to capture and kill as many individuals as possible no matter of what type, and to promptly convert them into life-sustaining food. Then as now, man no doubt preferred certain parts of an animal, and thick juicy steaks from the haunch of a defunct Bos tickled the ancestral palate, as similar cuts delight ours today. The great beasts were also easy to kill and could have been, and undoubtedly were, driven whenever possible into some impasse from which there was no escape except by leaping over a precipice to their immediate destruction. Vast numbers of the hapless creatures perished, one imagines, in just this manner, a type of slaughter later practiced so successfully by our own Indian tribes when bison roamed the great plains and rolling country of the North American continent.

To Cro-Magnon cave artists, interested as they were in depicting various game animals, the magnificent wild ox was of course an inspiration not to be disregarded by these sensitive and impressionable savages. As models, the cattle were among the best. They could be fairly easily approached, and their striking contours made splendid subjects for delineation on the cavern walls. Such images, therefore, are quite commonly found in the grottoes of France and Spain, and a series quite recently discovered near Les Eyzies are especially well drawn and full of the peculiar bovine character. As the pictures are in color, we see that a kind of silvery-gray, spotted with small patches of black, represented one color variation, the other being an all-over dark reddish black, very much like that of a present-day Devon ox. From an artist's point of view, one wonders why these drawings so closely resemble either a cow or an ox and not a bull in their silhouettes. Certainly in our domestic breeds the difference in contour is very apparent—the bull of any variety being much thicker and heavier in the neck region, with fine small hindquarters. Our oxen on the contrary lean towards the feminine in their profile, with the thin neck, slim horns, and larger hindquarters of the domestic cow. It goes without saying that there is some explanation for these discrepancies in form, but as we shall see later in the description of the animals domesticated by the Swiss Lake Dwellers, the origin of practically all tamed animals is lost in the fog of antiquity.

The range of *Bos primigenius* was not confined strictly to the European continent, but extended far to the east, which was, no doubt, the point of origin for the species. They were among the most useful of all the many great types of wild animals roaming the plains and forests of our earlier world as a source of food and clothing. Evidently, the heavily muscled carcasses of the great brutes provided no end of splendid nourishment, and the leg bones were not only cracked for the marrow they contained, but later carved and decorated or made into harpoon and spear points, fishhooks, needles, and many other articles of man's household economy. The tough hides also possessed valuable properties. Stretched on a wooden frame, they made boats of a sort, and tanned and softened, nothing was finer for clothing of every kind. The great pliable skins, spread over proper supports, served splendidly for huts or tents in severe weather. Old *Bos primigenius,* wild-eyed and long of horn, must then have been a real Godsend to our ancient relatives.

EUROPEAN BISON AND THE REINDEER

No history of early man in Europe would be complete without some special mention of the great variety of grazing animals existing apparently in vast herds during the long glacial and interglacial periods which in succession covered large sections of that continent. To the presence of these splendid creatures, man in a very practical way owes his existence during those strenuous times. The question

of sufficient food is, after all, paramount wherever
life is concerned, and primarily so to our ancestors
because during the frigid ages the climate of Europe
was never mild enough to encourage the growth or
ripening of fruits or berries, certainly not in sufficient quantity to appease the hunger of a horde of
voracious savages. To these active aborigines the
bison, the reindeer, and the horses and wild cattle
were very frequently all that stood between them
and starvation. As figured so adequately by the Cro-
Magnon artists, the great shaggy form and horned
head of the bison present a majestic and striking
appearance, and the herd of these magnificent beasts
painted on the ceiling at Altamira (and described
more fully elsewhere in this book) shows clearly the
various details of their postures, forms, and color.
The animal today is on the verge of extinction, at
least in a wild state, but it may be brought back by
careful breeding and protection, in the same way
that our own species (locally known as the buffalo)
has been saved from complete annihilation.

In the reindeer (*Rangifer tarandus*) we see quite
another but equally valuable animal in the economy
of ancient man. Vast herds of these cold-resistant
creatures wandered over the hills and vales of central
and southern Europe during several periods of the
glacial epoch. They came from the north always,
following closely in the wake of the coldest years

of those frigid centuries and retreating northward again as balmier weather prevailed in the interglacial times of the great ice age. Both males and females of the species carry horns, a unique trait in the deer family, and the widely spreading hoofs support the creature when passing over snowy ground. Their food consists mainly of reindeer moss and other cold-weather plants, and they are said to scrape away very deep snow in order to get at the coveted food. The reindeer of Europe and Siberia no longer exist in a wild state, but the Greenland species and our own so-called Caribou, as well as the Newfoundland variety, still roam the colder parts of their chosen habitat. To our ancestors, the reindeer in their thousands were an assurance of sufficient food in the cold, hard eras of a difficult world.

THE RED STAG

Fortunately for animal lovers, the splendid red deer (*cervus elaphus*) has come down to us through the ages in practically the same form as that seen by our European forefathers. Before and during the lives of these ancient beings, the beautiful creatures evidently roamed the forests and glades of both Europe and Western Asia, as their remains are found in widely separated sections of the two continents. They were a persistent race, living under the stress and change of many varying climates. In their usual intensely practical way, stone-age men considered them excellent sources of food, while their great tined antlers provided the hunter or the artisan with a tough, hard, bony substance from which were manufactured many objects of great utility such as spear and arrow points. As a kind of socket for the insertion of the stone hatchet, they were unsurpassed, and needles, knives, pushers for retouching flint tools, and many other types of valuable utensils could be easily fashioned from them by a clever hand. No wonder, then, that the chase of the stag, considered a sport by modern man, was to his ancestors a very important objective in their daily search for a living.

In recent times the red stag has practically disappeared as a wild animal from most of its former range, though there is still a large wild race living in the Caucasus. The animal is not as large as the American elk, but it is a formidable fighter when cornered or wounded, and the sharply pointed antlers can inflict terrible damage upon another buck of its own species or upon any other animal which approaches too closely.

All through the late Stone Age, stags were hunted probably with dogs domesticated by man. Dogs served not only as companions, but as most valuable assistants in the pursuit of wild game. Together man and dog made a powerful and aggressive combination of force, determination, and sagacity, the various physical and mental attributes of each well supplementing those of the other. Numbers of men took part in these exciting forays because the killing of an animal so fleet and powerful as the stag required not only skill with the spear or the bow but tremendous stamina as well. With the dog as a helper, such difficult feats could be more easily accomplished as the fierce but intelligent canine not only followed the fleeing quarry by sight, but could distinguish its whereabouts by scent whenever it became invisible in the thick cover. In this way it could be brought to bay and distracted until the hunters might finally manage to kill it with a club or spear thrust or a well-directed arrow. We can affirm that our early progenitors could and did feel the thrill of such a fracas, and the consequent satisfaction at the death of their horned adversary is quite understandable to thousands of modern nimrods who have infinitely less reason for destroying the magnificent creature.

Today the red deer still roams over large areas of the Scottish highlands, and until war devastated so many European countries there were herds in the private preserves in Germany, Austria, and various central European countries. These herds, however, while free to range at will through vast stretches of woodland and mountain country, were nevertheless not really wild in the true sense of the word. For in the fall, at which time the bucks had fully developed their splendid sets of antlers, they were driven by beaters and gamekeepers towards selected spots where numbers of them were shot down as they rushed madly by the rows of enthusiastic hunters gathered to enjoy the age-old sport. In these brutal and totally unnecessary killings, we may see again that peculiar lust for destruction so inherent in the human race. We can excuse the cave man, driven as he was by constant hunger, but in our time no such extenuating circumstances can be cited in defense of this kind of procedure.

To some modern eyes at least, there is a vast deal of charm about the stag and his hind, and the graceful, agile creatures figure largely in the romances, verses, and pictures of both Scotch and English writers and animal painters. The red stag, especially, is singled out from the other European species (roe, buck, fallow deer, and elk) as representing the epitome of all that is majestic and soul-inspiring in the deer family. This partiality is not surprising because the animal displays an astonishing amount of dignity and character as it poses in various alert and striking attitudes, usually amid the wild and picturesque surroundings of mountains, vales, and rushing streams. The bright colors of its smooth, shining coat blend harmoniously into this lovely background. The general effect of such a picture often stirs within the souls of sensitive individuals a strong nostalgic urge to become once more a part of the wonderful pageant of nature, coupled with an intense desire to throw off the shackles of civilization and to revel in that sensation of freedom and freshness of vision which is one of the rarest treasures lying deep within the heart of man.

THE APE FAMILY

Of the existing great apes—gorilla, chimpanzee, and orangutan—the latter is by far the most consistent lover of the treetops as his permanent home. In the dense tropical forests of Borneo and Sumatra, he seldom if ever comes to the ground, preferring to remain in safety and comparative solitude, sheltered by the dense vegetation. There, feeding on fruits and nuts and occasional birds' eggs, he ekes out a quiet arboreal existence. Strange in character is this "man of the woods," uncouth in appearance, and singularly apathetic in his movements as he swings slowly but powerfully through the liana-bound branches, employing the smaller ones in weaving a clumsily made bed as darkness gathers in the evening sky. Long, coarse hair of a distinctly reddish tinge covers his rather delicately fashioned body, but a veritable fringe of the same unusual color hangs from his long and heavily muscled arms. A great sack or collar of loose skin droops over the breast from the sides and front of the neck, and the adult males of a certain type develop enormous growths at either side of the face, giving the visage a platterlike shape. All in all he is a being grotesque in the last degree but remarkably reticent in character, especially for an ape.

In the days of very early man, perhaps 500,000 years ago, the area occupied by orangs and many other species of animals now confined to island localities was vastly greater than at present. Indeed, we know that the great chain of tropical islands, Sumatra, Java, Borneo, perhaps New Guinea, were all joined to the mainland of Indo-China and India. Giant extinct apes, the probable ancestors of all our modern types, are found in India proper, while the teeth of ancient orangs are common in the druggists' shops of China. The ancient man-ape, *Pithecanthropus,* then existed in the forests of Java, and at times must have come face to face with the great long-armed orang, leering at him from a tree branch. Then there was a mutual appraisement, each wondering what manner of creature the other represented. While *Pithecanthropus* could climb even better than a modern man, he was a mere amateur at the game when compared to the long-armed simian. On the other hand, he possessed many advantages both structurally and mentally to which the orang apparently never aspired. He could, for instance, walk and run on the forest floor in an upright position, and his mental reactions extended far beyond the plane of the huge red ape's capabilities in that direction. Apparently, as we now know, the man-ape's mind was to keep on developing through all the long ages of its future history. His flattened head was to become in time a domelike object filled with a super-quality of gray matter, a characteristic foreign to the orang's story of evolution. For in that being gazing upward so fixedly at the big monkey there lay potentialities of advancement beyond our under-standing, on whom already shone the bright rays of a higher world of thought and physical accom-plishment.

NEOLITHIC CULTURES, SWISS LAKE DWELLERS AND THE EARLY BRONZE AGE

There are many blank and vague spots occurring in the story of man's rise to civilization. No one knows exactly where or when the Old Stone Age (that is, the age of chipped but unpolished imple-ments) ceased to exist, but there was very probably no sharp division between that period and the follow-ing, so-called New Stone Age, or the time of polished utensils, one merging into the other imperceptibly. However, a very marked cultural change was evident in the nature of the invading races then entering Europe from several directions, and certainly art for art's sake, at least as understood by the Cro-Magnons, was by this time relegated to a very minor place in man's economy. These encroaching races appear to have been a highly industrious people, knowing and employing many household crafts in a very proficient manner, so that the sum total of their achievements began to reach vast proportions. As the New Stone Age progressed, the beautifully finished and polished hand axes became more and more common. Evidently man's efforts to attain the finer things of life had begun to bear fruit.

Soon most of Europe was teeming with the activities of great hordes of newcomers from many different sources. East, North, and South were contributing their share of energetic, intelligent, and highly progressive peoples all eager to participate in whatever the region had to offer in the way of food, clothing, tools, and weapons. Then as now housing problems confronted these masses of humanity. Villages of huts were constructed on strategic hillsides or in marshy country where water barriers were great aids to all peacefully inclined inhabitants by preventing sudden attacks from hostile neighbors and dangerous wild animals. For in spite of the increasing masses

of human inhabitants, the wide forests and plains of
Europe still contained ferocious flesh eaters, as well
as enormous herds of big game, cattle, deer, horses,
wild boars, etc., whose flesh supplied man with excellent food while the furry skins were fashioned into
suitable clothing. In Switzerland, especially, industry
rose to a high pitch and the houses of the Lake
Dwellers during the Polished Stone Era, as also in
the succeeding Bronze and Iron Eras, were perfect
hives of human energy and ambition. Man in the last
analysis had become a worker, a producer, and a
mighty force in world history.

It is surprising, indeed, to realize how in this comparatively early stage of man's existence he had so
tremendously complicated his scheme of living. A
survey of what he was accomplishing shows how
wide a range of activities occupied the mind and
physical energies of this extraordinary mammal.
Apparently there was nothing he couldn't and
wouldn't attempt in the line of his ambitious endeavors for self-improvement. The mere growth of
the number of individuals in a given community is
astonishing to a modern observer, especially since,
during the remote periods under discussion, man's
inability to cure himself of either wounds or disease was hardly an asset in his successful race for
survival. He must have been, in very truth, a tough,
resilient, and courageous being, able to stand hard

knocks from whatever quarter they were delivered
and to rise superior to many of them in spite of dis-
couragement, pain, and all the other ills of the flesh.
Naturally it was the survival of the fittest, and only
the strongest or the luckiest survived. Yet nothing
could keep man down for long, so great were his
recuperative powers, his boundless ego, and his tremendous urge to travel afield.

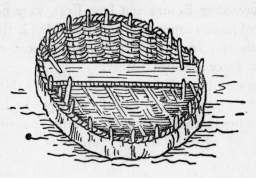

Coracle afloat

Each new accomplishment—a sturdier boat, a
finer spear, a sharper hatchet, or a more powerful
bow—was a contributing factor in this constantly
ascending living scale. Once he had set himself upon
the long road of material progress, there was no
end to his plans and prospects—his sea trips and
battles with strange tribes, his failures, and above all
his victories. Victory, of course, spelled domination,
defeat meant slavery, which was precisely what the

word implied in the formative eras of which we speak, and language, whatever it was, began to be a tremendous force for good or evil in the course of man's life. Then as now the mass psychology of crowds was felt, understood, and taken advantage of in the swaying of man's thoughts and subsequent actions.

Nevertheless, we must not forget in any review of our early history that all parts of the world were not equally advanced in a material or even a mystical or religious way. Thus we know that Egypt and the countries bordering on the southern Mediterranean had a highly developed, quasi-civilized population long before this desirable condition had reached the northern side of the big sea. At the same time, much of northern Europe was still locked in the ice masses remaining from the last great glacial era, with the result that the peoples and races were still in a decidedly primitive state of culture. This is an important point to remember because the very fact of such a condition was responsible for the swift acceleration of what we know as trade or barter between widely separated peoples and tribes. The successful carrying out of these transactions, whether large or small, has always apparently been a moving force in man's economy, certainly from the times of his earlier existence when he had advanced mentally to a point where such transactions were made possible by the use of boats, rafts, or organized land excursions of some duration. Only by accepting as a fact such methods of interchange between peoples can we account for the finding in many of man's ancient homesites of articles such as ambers, sea shells, types of flint, and many other definitely foreign objects which were unknown in the particular region where the excavations have been carried out.

The urge to trade or exchange one desirable possession for another is a very early characteristic peculiar to the human mind. Primarily, it might well have stemmed from a desire to take advantage of the other fellow, a very human trait but an understandable one in view of man's superior acuteness and determination to win against any opposing force. We must remember in this connection that not all tribes or peoples were equally developed in their efforts to develop trade relations with their neighbors. Certain types of early man, such as the Swiss Lake Dwellers, were apparently devoted to the particular region which they inhabited. Therefore, we find in the debris accumulated in the lake beds what are evidently the remains of a very long occupation of these highly desirable dwelling stations. Beginning with the late stone period, these people progressed slowly through the succeeding Bronze Age and finally emerged into what is known as the Iron Age of human achievements. However, as already related, these conditions occurred long after similar cultures had been experienced by peoples and races living in the warmer and more equable climate of northern Africa, regions where man might easily have existed in physical comfort and consequently have had more leisure to develop the higher brackets of his extraordinarily brilliant mind.

Although our very ancient relatives had progressed to a certain degree through the years of their residence on earth, it was not until they had actually emerged into the truly human state that a profound advance is noticeable in their various accomplishments. Leading the van of the newer period in man's occupation of Europe, the Cro-Magnons may be said to have embodied in their anatomical proportions practically all of man's physical evolution as far as we know it, even to the present day. We have shown, however, that in the making of utensils and implements they were rather futile, devoting much of their energies to an esthetic expression of the animal life of the time. To these great people we owe a vote of thanks in more ways than one because their productions tell us the presence of a phase of our mentality which otherwise would not have been apparent until much later in human history. In other words, the Cro-Magnons stressed the mystical, introspective side of man's nature, even though they virtually ignored the practical approach.

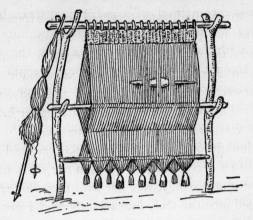

Primitive Loom with Weights, Distaff and Spindle

For ages after the disappearance of these talented savages, man still continued the use of stone implements and weapons, and we have told of the discovery of bronze and its various uses in a minor range of activity. It is difficult to realize, however, the enormous potentialities of this metal and how it enabled man to increase in every way the scope and scale of his productions. There is one curious trait, perhaps partially sentimental, which makes it difficult for man to abandon completely the use of any once-discovered materials—stone, bone, ivory, wood or whatever the substance may be. He has, also, a very decided facility for combining one material with another in the production of his manufactured articles. Thus, we observe in the lake dwellers a consistent method of constructing their habitations of wood and thatch, building the huts upon wooden platforms set up on piles over the water. Even though we may regard these people as in the first stages of the Bronze Age of their culture, as yet the metal was employed only in objects where its qualities were of the greatest value. At the same time they continued to manufacture their boats of wood, their nets of flaxen cord, the clothing of wool and flax, and the pottery usually of clay. Implements still remained in the polished stone stage, especially the axes and adzes. Stone spear points and swords and daggers, on the contrary, were no longer considered adequate, and beautifully formed weapons in the cast bronze technique now took their place— all far more valuable as fighting implements and in the killing of wild animals. A true civilization, even though in its primitive stage, had appeared upon the shores of these shining mountain lakes and would continue to develop along consistent lines for thousands of years until the discovery and the use of iron succeeded bronze in the manufacture of many things.

Not much change, however, was indicated in the construction of the dwelling huts. They were still made of wood and set up on the inevitable piles. On the shore in the vicinity of the dwellings, men turned up the soil and oxen were employed to drag the heavy wooden plow through the deep furrows. The live stock grazed peacefully on the sweet, natural grasses. The cattle, sheep, goats, and horses wandered about on the higher ground, while the grunting swine sought out the low watery levels nearer the lake shore. On the glassy surface of the big lakes men paddled dug-outs to and fro from the landing stages to fishing nets set in fairly deep water. There was a certain romantic quality about the sylvan landscape, though such emotions hardly had a place in the minds of the Lake Dwellers themselves. Life in those days was a strictly realistic affair, yet here in man's habitations by these placid sheets of glacial waters, three vital scenes in the drama of man's existence had already been enacted.

Pile Dwellings of the Neolithic Age

The Polished Stone or Neolithic Era had been the first; the second, a gloriously inventive period

when bronze had revolutionized the living facilities of the race, and now the iron period of man's culture had come into its own. Little bellows-blown furnaces heated and melted the crude ore, smiths pounded the softened glowing metal into sword blades, sickles, hoes, spear points, and fishhooks, horseshoes, pincers, and a thousand other useful articles. We shall leave these industrious people, whose origin is still a mystery, to the enjoyment and profit which accrued from their untiring energy and resourceful manner of living. For they now have reached a stage in human progress very little below many so-called civilized races at the present time.

In the British Isles, lake, marsh, and sidehill dwelling places were also in the full tide of bronze and early iron age activity, and the northern or Scandinavian regions of Europe were making their share of cast objects in bronze and iron, many of them highly artistic as well as useful.

And their well-made wooden boats enabled these hardy northern savages to make long and dangerous trips to new lands across wide seas and beautiful bronze horns, long and gracefully curved, were produced by these expert founders of the highly useful metal. Bronze was also used for making an endless succession of weapons, pieces of horse harness, shields, helmets, armor, pots, urns and jewelry, as well as every conceivable household utensil,

Wagon from the Bronze Age (Denmark)

both practical and ornamental. Man simply reveled in his newly found metallic treasures, bronze and in later periods iron, because with these intensely hard but (when heated) extremely adaptable substances he could hew his logs for houses, boats and weapons, and whenever necessary, cut stone itself into any form he wished to produce for building his tombs, his homes, and his fortifications. Our ancestor had at last in very truth attained the full stature of a man.

DOMESTIC ANIMALS

The problem of the physical origin of domestic animals has been one of great difficulty, though on the face of it an easy solution would seem probable. It does not appear likely that man began to bring wild animals under his domination until some period in the later stone age. But from all the data available on the subject, which strictly speaking is very meager in character, the dog heads the list as the first of the wild creatures to attach itself to the abode and the personality of man. This attachment, we may well believe, was to a certain extent mutual and beneficial to both of the principals concerned—the dog perhaps attracted by the smell and the sight of flesh when luck had favored the early hunter, and the man quick to recognize in the brute the high intelligence and a certain peculiar friendliness to members of the human species. We may thus speak quite confidently of the method of the dog's introduction into the homes of early man, but the wild ancestor of that intelligent creature has thus far eluded identification by scientists. Presuming that some wild species in the far east first developed domestic proclivities, what can that species be and where is its home today?

No answer has as yet been found to this apparently simple question, though various theories have been advanced by experts such as the great Charles Darwin and many others. Darwin seemed to think that this elusive ancestor might have belonged to a wild species now extinct, but one can hardly accept this solution as possible because of many difficulties thus far not yet satisfactorily explained. Today, none of the creatures listed technically as wild dogs bear more than a superficial resemblance to any domestic races, though in the wolves and jackals we can trace a strong resemblance to such recent breeds as the chows, police dogs, collies, eskimos, and spitz varieties—all types with upright pointed ears, heavy coats, and brushlike tails. Where the Australian dingo actually came from, no one seems to know, but in the writer's opinion it is perhaps nearer than any other modern breed to an original wild dog progenitor. We can not think that the dog of the

Swiss Lake Dwellers was anything more than a kind
of degenerate wolf or jackal, accustomed to the
presence of man and therefore not afraid of his two-
legged masters. This statement, however, is mere
supposition because we know him only by the skeletal
remains found associated with those of stone-age
man in the muddy deposits of the Swiss Lake
bottoms.

But whenever and wherever the dog first appeared, it didn't take him long to fall into the ways
of his human companions to whom he endeared himself by his courage and intelligence, coupled with a
strange but most useful peculiarity in that he regarded his owner's person and domicile as sacred
and would defend both with the utmost tenacity
against all comers. This last trait has always been
regarded by man as of outstanding merit in the
canine character, and the "watchdog" and his sleep-
less vigilance have been a part of man's story for
thousands of years.

There are several other species of large and useful
animals found in the Swiss Lake bone beds, viz.,
horses of two or more races, cattle, pigs, sheep, and
goats; all probably at one time or another brought
under man's surveillance and at least partial domestication. At first, apparently, this assortment of
beasts was merely confined, bred, and eaten when
hunger pressed the clans; but later, and after man

had drifted slowly into a more pastoral condition of living, cattle and horses were no doubt used as beasts of burden, or to drag a rude plow across hitherto untilled pieces of land.

The origin of these various stocks, however, is still an unanswered mystery. The pig, for example, is not the descendant of the European wild boar whose young are always horizontally striped brown and white; nor can the ancient relatives of the domestic goat and sheep to be found wild in any country today. As to the cattle, here again the obvious answer would be that they came from the great *Bos primigenius* of Europe. On examination, however, this is shown not to be the case, and the best that science can do today is to seek for some far eastern, but elusive relative as the ancestor of our domestic breeds. Much speculation, mostly by prejudiced writers, has been indulged in over the years, and such breeds as the white Chillingham cattle of England, the longhorned Scottish type, and many others all have their sincere but not especially well-informed proponents whose ideas on the subject, while interesting, are not basically conclusive.

In the larger sense, however, the influence of the domestication of several types of useful animals upon our lake-dwelling relatives is of the very highest importance in our study of ancient man as a progressing creature in a thousand different fields of activity.

The mere fact that he, after his ages of wandering, his long migrations from distant places, and a generally unsettled mode of living, should have had the desire to settle down permanently in any one spot is in itself of a most astounding reversal of his usual method. It is possible and indeed probable that once man had discovered the manifold advantages of this type of existence he, with his usual astuteness of perception, realized that here was the kind of life he had been seeking for thousands of years—some spot that he could definitely call "home" with its buildings, flocks and herds, a family, and the means of securing a thoroughly permanent and adequate food supply, a kind of alpine Utopia of his own making.

RELIGIOUS BELIEFS

We have thus far spoken only casually of the mystical and religious side of man's character, but that such thoughts occupied a large part of his leisure time is a foregone conclusion to any student of the subject. The type of mind capable of dwelling upon such matters is evident from very early times in our history, though the explanation of the desire for such reflections remains as ever a mystery. There is always extreme complication in trying to elucidate

man's actions and the inner emotions which prompt
those actions. For our purpose, we can glance only
at the outward manifestations of these profound
and vital inspirations. Whether early, prehuman
types of the Peking, *Pithecanthropus* class were far
enough advanced mentally to have more than a
smattering of abstract thoughts, we have no means
of knowing. One would visualize them as being unable to grasp anything outside of the purely realistic phase of existence, though certain great natural
forces—wind, rain, thunder, lightning, and volcanic
action—might all, by their tremendous exhibition of
power, have made some sort of impression upon their
limited mentalities.

However, in the Trois Frères cave in southern
France, there exists that wonderful painted mural
figure of the so-called Sorcerer, he of the stag-horned
head, bear's-paw hands, painted legs, and long tail.
With the finding of this grotesque image, our actual
knowledge of the presence of a mystical side to man's
inner nature has at last been confirmed, but we must
realize that naturally this representation was not
by any means the first of such images to be conceived,
and is unique simply because others have not yet been
discovered. But it is strange that we have not found
many more such renderings of mythical forms, considering the number of caves and grottoes in France
and Spain which contain the animal murals, and

Great Irish elk pursued by early Swiss spearmen

Early Swiss Lake Dwellers driving their herds

where plenty of wall space was available for the setting down of any pictures that came into the mind of the Cro-Magnon artists. These drawings were, of course, the contributions of men very much like ourselves in every way, and not by any means the product of a limited mentality. The significance of this stylized bit of mural artwork is what specially interests us here, because the figure clearly depicts a kind of witch doctor and suggests a type not clearly indicated in any of the other paintings made by this race of prehistoric men. Idol and fetish worship is still practiced to this very day in many outlying sections of the world, so that evidence of it in the old French grotto is of the first importance to anthropologists generally.

There is and apparently always has been a curious mixture of personal ego, superstition, fear, and downright ignorance in man's approach to any subject which he could not clearly understand. Among life's enigmas there has always been the peculiar revulsion against death and final annihilation. All animals possess this very necessary quality to a certain degree because without it the mere strain of existence would eventually prove too difficult for even the lowliest of created beings. Every moving thing, no matter how minute, is thus endowed with a desire to live out its life span. Because man has been for ages the most brainy and ambitious of vertebrates, he has naturally elaborated on this ambition and devised all sorts of schemes for even further perpetuating his own personality in spite of every obstacle which nature could place in his way. His efforts in this direction have naturally been expressed in many different methods of approach to such a serious subject, but the underlying reason for all of them has been to assure himself on this crucial point.

The unique power of projecting his thoughts and reflections beyond the actual premises of an earthly environment is no doubt the basis for his many mystical and religious beliefs, these being very deeply seated in his profound and complicated mental reactions to every phase of living. Even the low-browed Neanderthal peoples participated in these fundamental characteristics of man's personality because they too buried their dead with attention to ritualistic detail, as is proved by the presence of flint weapons in the burial sites, and the carefully arranged position of the skeleton fragments which have been unearthed in various regions in France and in the near East. Thus early in man's history we become aware of the inner workings of an individual ego, perhaps the most precious (if rightly controlled) of all his extraordinary qualities. We of a modern generation who live in a world obsessed very largely with the idea of material gain can hardly envisage the prominent part played by this mixture of personal ego, religious enthusiasm, and strict ceremonial in the lives of our ancestors. Today we may realize, by concrete evidence in the form of tombs, monuments, and temples, the importance attached to the proper observance of all such manifestations of reverential expression.

In the days of man's earlier existence, when both his powers of concentration and physical skills were limited, we see only slight suggestions (such as the careful Neanderthal interments) of any desire to perpetuate himself after death, but as time went on and actual manlike beings became dominant, there was a mounting effort to elaborate suitable memorials for the spirits of the departed. Great single stones, groups of stones, mounds of various sizes and shapes, and finally buildings, crude at first and becoming more and more elaborate, bear witness to man's desperate desire for some measure of immortality. The great mounds of earth accumulated by some early American peoples and found in many parts of the United States are definite examples of this universal yearning for a future existence and the Maya, Aztec, and Inca edifices consecrated to religious purpose are among the very finest examples of early architecture in the entire world.

Insofar as sorcery is concerned, the very first glimpse of the painted figure of the sorcerer in the Trois Frères cave in Southern France opened our eyes to a phase of man's character which was evidently a part of his deeper personality. Whence came the unique desire even in that early time to discover some link between the known facts of existence and a future world of wishful dreams and ambitions? If we knew the answer to that question, it might solve many things that still remain a mystery in the study of the human animal both past and present. Whenever man's supernatural yearnings began to assume some importance in his scheme of living, it became necessary to employ a medium, or medicine man, to rightly interpret the desires of the person making the appeal and to make clear the results of mysterious interviews with higher beings in the nether world. It was believed that these, if properly approached, might grant special dispensations to favored suppliants for help of every kind. Thus were the cults of witchcraft, sorcery, and superstition born into the world—cults so persistent and all-enthralling in their various expressions that even in our own day they still flourish under endless guises and disguises in every inhabited region of the globe.

A JOURNEY IN PREHISTORY

The summer of 1927 was to be a memorable one for the author and his family because of a unique invitation received from Henry Field, then a young

anthropologist of the Field Museum in Chicago, to
accompany him on a trip to some of the better-
known caves in France and Spain, where drawings,
paintings, and sculptured forms of animals, made
by a race of prehistoric men, were to be seen in all
their pristine freshness and excellence of execution.
These wonderful examples of ancient art had been
produced thousands of years ago by the Cro-Magnon
people.

Our mentor and guide in this truly romantic adventure was to be the Abbé Henri Breuil, celebrated
savant from the Collège de France and world expert
on the art and general culture of prehistoric man.
It was our good fortune to be thus associated with
one of the very ablest men on this subject. An eminent
scientist with a genial and interesting personality,
he had previously visited all the caves which we
were to examine and had faithfully copied many of
the drawings and paintings they contained.

We had agreed that all of us should meet at Les
Eyzies, a tiny hamlet in Southern France not far
from the rail station of Périgueux on the Paris-
Lyons-Mediterranean route to the Riviera. The
Dordogne region in which Les Eyzies lies is world-
famous for its many caves and rock shelters, the
former homes of a host of prehistoric peoples who
left great quantities of interesting implements and
works of art. Here also were found a number of

actual skeletons, practically complete, of two early races of man, the Neanderthal and Cro-Magnon.

Under the Abbé's careful surveillance, we were to busy ourselves with delightful excursions in and about this charming region, drinking in its beauties, learning much ancient history upon the original sites where it had its being, and generally enjoying ourselves to the full in the midst of a pleasing and always stimulating company of fellow scientists from all parts of the world. However, as we descended from the train at Périgueux on a very warm and glowing afternoon, these events all lay ahead of us. Henry Field, good angel of our trip, met us and we walked across the deserted little plaza near the railroad to a restaurant of sorts, where we sampled for the first time a type of food with which my family at least was unfamiliar. As a starter we had potage, watery and tasting vaguely of chicken, served in a huge tureen with large chunks of bread floating about on its glistening, greasy surface. For meats, a choice of two —veal and ham—both anemic examples of what can happen to a calf or a pig when under the jurisdiction of a local cook; vegetables consisted of potatoes and cauliflower; then came dessert, some green hard filberts still in their husks. Wine, of course, was served, the usual cheap, red and sour. We drank bottled water, a flat-tasting liquid known as Evian, supposedly uncontaminated. The coffee was primarily chicory. Instead of tea, a pale whitish fluid, *du lait,* completed a typical menu with which we were to become well acquainted during our sojourn in this fair land.

After dinner we took a short ride in a very hard-springed car to Les Eyzies, which lying as it did under a full yellow moon gave an eerie and thrilling impression of the picturesque town. It was in this romantic atmosphere that we first met the Abbé Breuil, a short, dark, almost bald man with brilliant full eyes, an ingratiating smile, and an informal but courtly manner. Although a priest of the Jesuit order, he was not dressed in clerical garb, but wore a somewhat dilapidated suit of khaki clothes, the trousers tucked into leather leggins, and a pair of stout muddy shoes. He was a man of great cultivation, a keen and mischievous host, and a veritable mine of knowledge on many subjects. After supper, we all walked along the single village street, a narrow badly kept roadway, running at the foot of great cliffs, which rose in sharp dark silhouette against the brilliant orb of the moon. Just above the road and right against the mighty wall, tiny houses were visible, indicated by little glowing spots of light, with smoke coming out of the round, low chimneypots. We had never before seen houses built in this manner directly against the cliff's face, the rear wall being the rock itself. But during our stay in this strange region, we were to come upon all sorts of new and unusual sights, both natural and man-made. Here was a place where the ancient world seemed not so very far removed from the human types of which we were a part for the time being. When the night was fully upon us, the air grew stifling with the approach of a tremendous thunder shower, accompanied by a drenching downpour. It seemed a fitting introduction to a world of life now evidenced only by the drawings and skeletal remains of the men and animals of another day.

A sky of brightest blue greeted us as we awoke the following morning after a not too peaceful night. What with rain, heat, thunder and lightning, and a most vociferous rooster just under our window, there was room for improvement in our sleeping conditions. I complained about the rooster, only to learn later to my sorrow that a too-anxious-to-please host had disposed of the poor bird in order to conciliate a nervous patron.

We were to lose no time in our explorations of the caves; the Abbé had arranged all that. Never have I known a more restless, dynamic personality than he proved to be, a sort of caged scientific lion pacing to and fro when balked or thwarted in any way, and a most persistent and energetic worker. Breakfast eaten, we were bustled into waiting cars that were much in need of good springs, and off we went on our first tour of cave inspection. It happened to be in this case the justly celebrated Font-de-Gaume grotto, containing among many other drawings, the frieze of the woolly mammoths, already described in the chapter on prehistoric art. In the brilliant morning light, we drove along the road at the base of the high cliffs seen so dramatically outlined on the previous evening. On high terraces at the base of the undulating contours of the cliff face, we could now clearly make out the little houses of the local peasantry nestling closely against the scarred and overhanging masses of yellow, black, and gray limestone, towering high into the brightness of the summer sky above the miniature dwellings below. There were bits of green visible along the top of the cliffs, small trees and shrubs and coarse grass and vines hanging down at intervals. But in the main, the face of the stony barrier was bare and had a stained and weather-beaten appearance.

We noticed small dark holes in places along the cliff front, and were told that man-made caves behind them had sheltered the inhabitants of the region in the good old days of chivalry when lawless raids upon respectable townsfolk, and the plundering of a company of travelers, were merely pleasant episodes in the daily life of the countryside. The tiny village was bald and bare enough under the sunlight, neither stores, nor business, could be seen; only poverty and privation were written upon the seamed and tired faces turned to us as we jolted slowly along towards our destination. The ride was short, and as we turned an abrupt corner in the road, before us rose the majestic battlement which houses the well-known grotto of the Font-de-Gaume, most popularized and best known of all the great group of caverns in France and Spain. This then was our first glimpse of a scene upon which, even though under much sterner climatic conditions, the eyes of many generations of prehistoric man had once rested. Here in very early days the sturdy men of the old Neanderthal race had battled with some great cave bear or pursued the herds of reindeer, bison, and horses which swarmed thickly in the valleys. After them had come prehistoric artists, men of the Cro-Magnon race, with their chalks and gravers and little lamps, to make the wonderful series of drawings which we were now to see for the first time.

The walk to the cave was not at all difficult; a narrow but well-marked path led close under the huge rocks towering above us until we reached the cavern entrances, two oval holes or openings in the cliff side. Had not the Abbé personally conducted us, we would have probably been met by an old woman, a constituted guide to the grotto, who neither knew nor cared about the treasures within, being concerned

only with her tip, as she chattered volubly and igno-
rantly about each painting upon the long uneven walls
of the narrow gallery. Such nuisances, however, were
never consulted or even noticed by the Abbé, who in
his khaki cave costume swept proudly ahead of our
party. Quite the master of the situation, and prepared as no one else in the world could have been
prepared to show us about and tell us the strange
and exciting story of the paintings. It was a really
dramatic moment, only possible when staged by a
member of the Latin race, but we had been prepared
beforehand by Henry Field for the very often distinctly humorous, not to say, spicy descriptions of
the animals depicted so faithfully and lovingly by
the ancient cave artists. In their time, however, these
caves existed in a state of complete and absolute
blackness until broken by the fitful light of the tiny
lamps carried by the Cro-Magnon mural masters.
But nowadays these same walls reflect the light from
strings of small electric globes suspended above
them.

We had come far to see these productions and
we gazed with unalloyed enthusiasm and astonish-
ment at the long series of mammoths, bison, horses,
reindeer, and other creatures now long extinct in the
region, which were extraordinarily and dramatically
interesting. A majestic procession of woolly mammoths, head to tail, their great recurving tusks and

high foreheads giving one a distinct feeling of awe and admiration for the skill of the man who had painted and incised their curious outlines thousands of years ago. What had he thought as he laboriously cut those forms with a piece of flint into the softer substance of the cave wall? Was it for mere pleasure that he had so inscribed them or was he giving vent to a fervent wish for better hunting and immortalizing his wishes at the same time? We shall never know, and either reason might be the true answer to the question.

In his broken yet fluent English, the Abbé pointed out with his cane the special outlines of the mammoths superimposed upon earlier drawings of bison, horses, and reindeer. We listened carefully—it was an engrossing talk on prehistory. "You see," he said, "Zee hye—zee nois—zee maus—zee tronc—zee défenses—(pardon)—zee tusks—zee great igh ead and ump on zee back—zee tail, so short—zee bully (translated belly)—zee hin quartair." This latter word stumped us all for a moment (I dared not look at Henry Field, standing in the background), but soon it was clear—hind quarters, of course, and a favorite expression of the Abbé's who I think was very proud of the way in which he pronounced the difficult words. So he went from animal to animal. The mammoths, reddish in color and covered with their long drooping hair, came first naturally in the description, but the others, bison, etc., all received careful attention.

As we moved slowly towards the back of the long, but narrow crevice, I noted with wonder the very uneven wall surfaces and found it hard to imagine anyone selecting such a spot for the drawing of a long series of mammoth images. To an animal painter the bison was especially interesting. This was, of course, the European bison or wisent, an animal now practically extinct in Europe, and a taller and more ponderous creature than our own. The horses, too, with their upright manes and scrubby tails reminded one of the modern (*Przewalski*) types from Turkestan. Today they, as well as the great hairy mammoths, protected from the bitter winter climate by their masses of long reddish hair and wool, are extinct in this region. These latter creatures were to me intensely romantic, for I pictured in my mind's eye the artist, breaking off in the midst of his work and running to the cave entrance from which point of view he could see in the valley at his very feet the actual living specimens of the great brutes as they fed and wandered over the hard and frozen ground, trumpeting, playing, fighting—an inspiration for a personality now buried forever in the mists of time.

Had I been there I too would have seen them, a thought which almost took my breath away. A sharp exclamation from the Abbé brought me back to reality, but it was a totally blacked-out reality, for the simple reason that the electric light had suddenly gone out and there we all stood petrified in total darkness! There was no danger, we all knew that, because the path to the entrance was almost straight and the cave was comparatively small, but the sensation was an eerie one and conjured up strange fancies in one's mind. Who was this man, warm, breathing, who stood so close to me in the Stygian gloom? Could the artist himself have come back to welcome us? Perhaps he'd been there all the time, and when the lights came on again we'd see him standing in our midst, tall, naked and magnificent with his bone palette in his left hand, the sharp flint graver held firmly in the other fist? On the floor at our feet a second man might be crouched, lighting a tiny stone lamp by striking two pieces of flint sharply together! Again the lights went on, and there were no people present other than our own little company, awed and slightly shaken by a glimpse into that long-past world of life.

Once more the Abbé was talking, telling me that if I were to go to the back of the cave and climb the little iron ladder standing against the wall I would see something I could never forget, as there was a drawing upon that wall, much finer than all the others and done by some other artist, a painting of a woolly rhinoceros, clear, strong and beautifully executed. Back I went, of course, climbed the iron steps, and then I saw it plainly, quite close to my head, brilliantly indicated and filled with life and animation. Correctly outlined too, the long low body and short legs, the hanging hair and little tail, and the curious hump, just at the back of the long head which, armed with its two sharp and boldly outlined horns, completed one of the very finest drawings in all the world of prehistoric art. It was a revelation indeed!

Our first experience in the study of cave art had been an impressive one but it was to be only the beginning of a series of delightful and edifying experiences, which were to follow in quick succession during the ensuing weeks of our sojourn in this land of wonders.

There are many other caves and rock shelters in the vicinity of Les Eyzies, not all with drawings or paintings, but nevertheless most valuable for a study of early man. Le Moustier, once occupied by people of the long-extinct and primitive Neanderthal race, was especially notable because of its situation on the highest of three terraces rising from the junction of two wide and shallow valleys. It possessed great possibilities for long-distance observation over a wide stretch of country for these crude, stockily built savages. Some years ago skeletal remains and implements of these ancient people were discovered near the base of the first terrace, but today the topmost cave has far more interest for the layman. We easily climbed the gradual ascent from the valley floor to the highest terrace, and there at the very corner of the sharply angled ledge came upon the grotto itself.

Its shape is peculiar, an almost square but not very deep depression cuts back into the cliff face, which is here quite low and extends but a few feet above the cave entrance before reaching the level of the plateau. The rock surface inside the shelter (it is hardly more than that) gives the impression of having been bored out by some great auger, the concentric planes of stony soil decreasing gradually almost to a point in the center of the cavern wall. There is nothing of interest now within the cave itself, but the view from the entrance across two valleys to the hills beyond is magnificent. In Neanderthal days this view would not have been quite the same as at present, because of a great difference in the local climatic conditions which then were severe, with much snow and rushing ice-filled rivers roaring by the meager little shelter.

The Abbé's insistent voice "Vite—vite!" and his tapping cane told us that it was time to return to the little hotel for dinner. Indeed food and plenty of it was never too far from the Abbé's thoughts, and it required an event or discovery of major importance to distract his attention from the hunger call so well developed in his stocky and efficient person. Naturally he wasn't alone in this worthy concentration upon the fleshpots, for all of us soon developed rather alarmingly good appetites under the aegis of constant activity.

Dinner at our domicile, I regret to say, was not all that the word implies. Food, such as it was, seemed to be quite abundant but there existed also a certain sameness in the menus from day to day. In clear weather we sat out of doors, the thin watery soup in the usual large tureens a prominent feature of these little banquets, while veal, string beans, and bread and more bread, followed by cheese and occasional knotty wormy little pears or bunches of grapes, concluded our repast. The staff of life in large circular loaves was cut individually at the table by placing the ponderous object close against the breast and slicing towards one's anatomy with a long sharp knife. This unwieldy portion of bread often fell on the ground, but it was promptly retrieved. A few chicken feathers and other encumbrances were removed from its surface and the operation imperturbably continued. All in all, however, and in spite of these slight distractions, the meals were enjoyed in a general atmosphere of cheerful good will. We shall never forget these simple repasts nor the unique and interesting surroundings. Across the street the small sawmill was sometimes cutting up French walnut logs for use in cabinetmaking, and an occasional train would wheeze slowly into the station close by and start again with the ear-piercing shrieks of its minute whistle, so different from the deep-throated bellow of our great expresses at home.

After a midday dinner we usually took a brief rest, unless the irrepressible Abbé had planned some special trip. In that case there would be frantic dressing and hurried calls before we climbed into the waiting cars. Sometimes it was a trip to some old and interesting town, such as Sarlat, ancient, dirty and different, redolent with unpleasant odors, but reminiscent of the old days of French kings, armored knights, and lovely ladies. We also visited Bugue, a modern and still dirtier town. Then there was La Roque Gageac, quaint, intensely strange and like something out of this world, with its tiny houses and streets jumbled closely together on the steep riverbank. On other days we inspected beautiful old and often ruined castles, perched aloft on the high plateaus above the valley and commanding superb views of the surrounding country. The scenery was extremely varied in character, but curiously enough except in rare instances could be seen only from some point in a valley and not from the high elevation of the general plateau. Indeed, today at any rate by far the greater part of peasant activities are confined to the valley environment, the higher land being dangerous and unprofitable to work, often with concealed crevices occurring at frequent intervals, while the soil is poor, harsh, and scantily covered with vegetation.

Les Eyzies has so many treasures and points of interest within its own little circle of antiquities that we lived in a kind of dizzy but strangely intriguing whirl as we enjoyed informative trips here and there to special places which showed evidences of the early occupancy of man. The country and its conformation was difficult to understand on first acquaintance, the roads running about in apparently rather aimless fashion first in the river valley and then on the high levels, but wherever we went it was all new to us and filled with a kind of nostalgic atmosphere of calm and ancient civilization. Even the peasantry seemed removed from the general run of French life, working hard at their own small tasks, somewhat dour, dissatisfied and rather Italian or Spanish in their general appearance. Many of the girls and younger women were very good-looking with masses of dark hair and tanned and rosy complexions. They toiled, as only a French peasant can toil, for hours in the hot sun, raising and tending their scanty crops, or engaging in village activities which ministered to the wants of the visiting scientists and a few French tourists who had chanced upon this little-known section of their own country. For it is a fact that most French people apparently have never heard of Les

Eyzies, or if they have it bears no interest for them. For the scientists, of course, this situation is one to be genuinely welcomed because it leaves them free to pursue their research activities in peace and without fear of distraction. Our party, gay and noisy, descended often like a bombshell upon these usually quiet centers of ancient culture. Always we had the Abbé, sprightly, unconventional, intense and vociferous, to show us everything—where the various layers of soil might be disclosed in a cutting at the base of one of the rock shelters and how experts carefully digging for and uncovering various accumulations of earth and bones and implements could read as from the pages of a book the successive life stories of men and animals who had once occupied the sites.

Many of the more valuable and informative of these objects now rest in the charming little Museum of Antiquities, which is situated on a rocky shelf above the street at Les Eyzies. Here, M. Peyrony, curator of the sanctuary, had been instrumental in forming some splendid collections of objects belonging to ancient man. Flint, hand axes, scrapers, gravers, and crude stone spearheads as well as images of animals in bone or ivory were all carefully labeled and exhibited to the best advantage. The local ancient history was thus very well demonstrated to the interested visitor, especially when the active and well-informed curator himself gave us the pleasure of his personal guidance. While looking over these examples of man's handiwork in the days of his earlier existence as a veritable human type, one must remember that at least two cultures are here represented. There are the crude and more roughly made artifacts of the very old Neanderthal people, as well as the more refined bone and ivory and stone implements later produced by the Cro-Magnon race whose splendid drawings we have just described.

M. Peyrony himself, presiding genius of the Les Eyzies region, was a man of a quiet though forceful personality, who actually was living at the time of our visit in a little house built close against and almost under the projecting curves of one of the great rock shelters. Why he preferred this ancient style of domicile I cannot say, because it is hard to conceive of a less desirable situation for one's homesite. Perhaps he wished to experience the difficulties under which his peasant neighbors had struggled for centuries, or (and more likely) there was a certain ascetic satisfaction to be sensed in thus submitting himself to such rigors. At any rate, there he was to be found when at home, he and his charming wife. He was strictly austere in his menage, although charming and hospitable and more than anxious to meet and entertain the Abbé's protegées with very illuminating talks on the life of his contemporaries in this small, remote, and very constricted community. In his youth, he said, there was only a central fire in the village, and often he had been obliged to carry burning embers to his father's home so that they might cook their frugal meals.

The days passed all too quickly for our party to which by now a photographer and a fellow artist had been added. But there were still any number of things to be seen—more caves, rock shelters, and no end of pleasant little excursions here and there as occasion offered. The tiny hamlet of St. Léon sur Vézère was at this time the headquarters of a group of anthropologists under the direction of Dr. George G. McCurdy, a well-known authority from Yale University. At St. Léon we had dinner amid charming surroundings, and listened to much expert discussion on the latest finds in the vicinity.

So far we had not seen, with the exception of some small pieces done in ivory or bone, any attempts at sculptures or carving, but now we learned that at a spot called Cap-Blanc there was a whole frieze (six in number) of splendidly modeled horses, about one-half life size and quite unique in every way. This proved to be a truly remarkable bit of prehistoric carving in high relief. The animals, spread along a wall of soft rock for a distance of thirty or forty feet, were exceedingly well executed and in addition showed a type of horse nearly comparable to the present wild horses of Turkestan (*Equus Prze-*

walski). My painting of three of these animals is done directly from the actual frieze and is not re-touched or improved in any way. The remarkably accurate silhouettes, showing the proportions and general contours of the animals, are full of life and required an expert artist. The curious upright mane, no forelock, and somewhat ratty tail of the modern Turkestan species is practically duplicated in these ancient sculptures, the finest things of their kind known to anthropologists. Fortunately, the whole line of animals was apparently covered for a long period by debris falling from the top of the cliff front, with the result that the delicately cut images were saved from weathering of any kind, and to this we may ascribe their almost perfect preservation after the lapse of thousands of years.

When the animals were first uncovered, a man's skeleton (possibly that of the artist who so cleverly produced these fine examples of late Cro-Magnon art) was found lying at the foot of the cliff just below the horse frieze. It did not look like an actual burial, and how he came to be there will always remain a mystery. But there was romance in this find, the association of a work of art with a being con-temporaneous with its production, one who had seen the sprightly little ponylike creatures in the flesh as they pranced and snorted, wheeled and galloped madly in an exuberance of animal spirits perhaps

10,000 years before our day. Such excellent examples of the work of ancient artists are really an inspiration to those of us who essay to follow in their footsteps, and one feels a real fraternal emotion in the presence of the sculpture and the meager remains of its possible producer.

It was a country for dreamy reverie about this prehistoric life now long passed away. However, after a brief spell the "Vite—vite!" uttered by the Abbé Breuil and emphasized with a tapping cane and a stamping, impatient foot broke rudely into these vaporizings as this dynamic son of the Church planned our activities and made arrangements for our visits to other and more distant fields of exploration.

One of the objects of our trip was the inspection and purchase by Henry Field of prehistoric remains, both human and man-made, for later exhibition in the Field Museum in Chicago, and we were more or less constrained to visit certain individuals known to the Abbé as possessing desirable collections for such an exhibit. But while we remained in Les Eyzies, our hurried round of cave explorations never stopped except when darkness fell across this wonderland of prehistory. The Combarelles Cavern, a remarkably long and very narrow cave was known to contain scores of interesting drawings along its 700-foot walls. Numerous species not in the Font-de-Gaume

grotto may be seen, including as many as 400 drawings, comprising an almost complete collection of
the mammals of the times. Lions, wolves, cave bears,
reindeer, bison, stag, ibex, rhinoceros, and several
crude renderings of the human form are inscribed
upon the stony surfaces. However, they do not reveal any unusual artistic ability; that is, they cannot
compare in accuracy with the rhinoceros of the Font-
de-Gaume cave, nor of many drawings elsewhere.
Nevertheless, they are all of intense interest because
every scrap of work of this far-off period is of vital
importance to the anthropologist, who is enabled to
see for himself a comprehensive exhibit of the fauna
existing contemporaneously with the human beings
of the last great glacial era.

"It's time," our guide proclaimed. "Time to be off
on our really long trip to the great cave of Altamira
in Northern Spain." En route we stopped to inspect
Isturitz, a small, warm, moist cavern in which we
saw a splendidly modeled figure of a reindeer, as
well as the bones of many cave bears and numerous
artifacts. Then on to Bayonne, home of the Hugue-
ñots. A lovely and interesting town which also contained a small museum, Le Musée Basque, filled with
examples of Basque art and household objects of
considerable antiquity and great interest. Our stay
here was a short one and we then had to prepare for

the long and difficult trip to Spain where the cavern of Altamira, one of the gems of prehistoric art, was to climax all that we had hitherto seen by the extraordinary number, size, and virility of the paintings upon its ceiling.

The first objective was Hendaye, our gateway to Spain on the French side of the border facing Irun. Two big cars with chauffeurs had been engaged, and we started on a fascinating ride across one of the spurs of the Pyrenees. The day was perfect, hot and clear, with blue sky and fleecy white clouds. At first we skirted the Bay of Biscay, lunching at San Sebastian, and later passed through Bilbao and other coastal towns before beginning the long ascent to the top of the big hills now closely pressing us on every side. Peaks and valleys, all lovely in color, succeeded each other in a never-ending procession, and toward dusk, as the full moon rose ahead of us over the crests, the effect was enchanting. The going was rough and sometimes precarious but we met practically no other cars on our way. As evening advanced, the higher sections of the road lay behind us, and a pretty tired, but still jovial little company was dozing and jolting about, shaken up at intervals and looking forward to a long night's sleep at Torre la Vega. The last fifty-mile stretch was a really glorious affair, for the great moon, brilliant beyond description, lighted up a superb land-

scape new to all of us except the Abbé, who, cheerful
and fresh as ever, kept everyone in good spirits by
his witty jokes and droll sayings. At last the town
and our hotel, and what a town it was! Though it
was decidedly late, the place was in full swing.
Lighted by a series of intensely brilliant and un-
shaded electric bulbs, the streets shone white in the
powerful glare, while the din was something to be
remembered.

Apparently no one in the entire community had
retired, and the hum of voices, singing, talking, and
laughing, combined with a constant street traffic and
music of all kinds, creating a real pandemonium of
sound which was hardly conducive to repose after
our eighteen-hour motor ride. The bedrooms, with
bare waxed floors seemed singularly unattractive.
This impression was doubly intensified when one
realized that the omnipresent flea was strictly on
the alert for a foreign invasion of the bedclothes
and promptly proceeded to take advantage of the
situation. By morning, after a terribly restless night,
we had a certain spotty appearance. However, nothing so trivial as the itch was allowed to interfere
with our trip, but we all breathed a sigh of relief
when the Abbé announced that we were leaving Torre
la Vega to take up our residence in the little village
of Santillana quite close to the great cave we had
come so far to see. It was welcome news, and we

proceeded to vacate Torre la Vega with all possible celerity.

A short ride brought us to a village so different in every way from the one in which we had passed the night that the change was more than appreciated. We obtained rooms in a newly opened, but expensive little hotel, formerly a de luxe hunting lodge for rich grandees of the royal entourage of Spain. The bed-rooms, surrounding a great salon on the second floor of the hostelry, were spacious and fairly comfortable. In spite of the newness of the place as a guest house, sanitary arrangements were scanty as usual, water always at a premium. One always wonders at the scarcity of water in European dwellings, especially when in most places there is such a surplus of it outside.

We were blessed, however, with clear weather, and for several nights a magnificent moon, shining with fierce intensity, created the most wonderful illusions of light and shade in the streets of this very ancient town. As one stood at the open window and gazed across the roofs of the little village, one's imagination inevitably pictured the life and times of another day, more especially as we listened entranced to a band of male singers wandering about the streets in the moonlight. Their natural singing compared favorably with the trained voices of the operatic stage. Sleep, at any time during the hours of darkness, seems entirely forgotten in Spain. Even the peasants apparently never went to bed except at noon for a short siesta. We could hear plainly on all sides the chatter and laughter of the peasant children as they gamboled about in the moonlight to the accompaniment of guitars and concertinas played by the old folks.

Bright and early on our second morning we were off on our journey to inspect the grotto of Altamira. It really was quite near and very accessible, at the top of a rising gradient a quarter of a mile from the road. The country was barren, dry, brown, and quite treeless, with squat and squalid, but extremely picturesque stone and stucco farmhouses at frequent intervals, while goats, few cattle, and donkeys grazed or wandered aimlessly about. Altamira, famed as one of the very greatest showplaces of prehistoric art, is with other caves and grottos under the supervision of the Spanish government, and we were fortunate in meeting Dr. Obermaier, a German Jesuit priest who was in charge of all such natural wonders throughout the country. The doctor had hurried up from Madrid principally to see his old friend and confrere, the Abbé Breuil, with whom in happier times in France he had been closely associated in a scientific way. He proved to be a most genial host and did everything in his power to make our trip comfortable. Count de la Vega, also deeply inter-

ested in the subject of prehistory, was our luncheon
host on this memorable occasion, and it was illuminating to us as Americans to see the almost feudal
ceremony which prevailed even during this little repast. To make matters still more monarchistic in tone
we were honored by a visit from the Duke of Alba,
royal head of all archaeological and historical monuments in Spain. As the Earl of Berwick in England
and heir to numerous other high and important titles,
this celebrated gentleman gave color and authority
to the visit of our little party, and we felt that in
Spain, at least in 1927, the monarchy stood on very
firm and popular ground. How soon this illusion was
to be rudely dispelled, King Alfonso and his English
queen deposed, and even the great Duke of Alba's
palace and possessions subjected to the despoiling
influences of a revolutionary regime under Franco,
people's champion and dictator!

But the cave and its treasures awaited us and
though we had been told by the Abbé that the work
was of the finest, I for one was tremendously impressed by the wonderfully outlined and richly tinted
bodies of the bison herd which romps so gaily over
the vast almost flat ceiling of the grotto. In 1879 or
1880 when the cavern was first examined, this ceiling
came down very nearly to the floor, so close I believe
that one could not stand upright in the narrow space
between the two surfaces. Today a ditch has been

dug around the base of the side walls and the cave is lighted by electricity, so that although its first appearance had been altered, one is now enabled to see clearly and admire these truly magnificent paintings. The figures are quite large, possibly half-life size and number about seventeen individuals of the bison species in various animated poses, two wild boars, a horse or two, and a female deer. At intervals on the ceiling large oval bosses of stone hang like flattened pillows from the main surface, and on these restricted areas the Cro-Magnon master has displayed some of his best talent, indicating with skill and ingenuity several of the great beasts lying down in attitudes characteristic of all cattle the world over. The paintings are amazingly spirited, bright and fresh in their tints of brown, reddish-ochre, black, yellow and white, the shadings beautifully accomplished and all done with a consummate ease and assurance hard to describe. They give the impression of having been tossed off in a fever heat of creational stress. The essentials of proportion, silhouette, varied pose, and color suggestion have been all controlled by a perfectly competent eye and an accurate and clever hand. In other words, a splendid piece of art was fashioned here under the most difficult and painfully restricted conditions. The cramped and awkward position made necessary by the close approximation of the floor to the ceiling surface on which the work is executed would be in itself a great detriment to bold and vigorous outline suggestion. But combined with this, of course, was the always meager lighting made possible only by a tiny stone lamp which shed its fitful glow over a vast, hard, and necessarily uneven background. In this case, at any rate, the artist was able to rise above his medium and environment and to set down the finest and grandest of all the artistic works of early man thus far discovered.

The romantic history of this find is interesting. A Spanish savant Sautuola and his daughter were one day searching as usual for weapons and other utensils on the rough floor of the cave when the child, looking upward suddenly, called the scientist's attention to some drawings just over their heads on the low ceiling. "Oh, papa, look at the bulls," was her classic way of summing up what she saw, but strangely enough the man was not especially interested in the revelation of this great artistic treasure so that for years the extraordinary find received but scant attention from the archaeological scientists. Indeed at one time the whole superb work was threatened by the blasting of some rock just above the ceiling of the grotto, an explosion which might have totally destroyed this magnificent relic in its entirety. Very fortunately, except for a few cracks that have since been repaired, no damage was done, thus preserving it for posterity.

Apotheosis of the Bronze Age

A prehistoric buffalo hunt by Indians of the Folsom Period

We lingered about this enchanted region for some days, being loathe to leave its many bizarre and little-known points of interest. The writer busied himself from morning until night painting some charming little scenes; a rustic farmhouse, the old and rare Romanesque cathedral in the town itself, and an inner courtyard of an old house where a tiny black donkey, standing beneath a ruined stone arch of great antiquity, gave a touch of life to an otherwise somnolent bit of ancient Spanish domain. The streets and the people were wonderful, the children little devils incarnate and mischievous as a pack of baboons. Every time they saw me emerge from the hotel with my easel and canvas they would scream like miniature furies, "Pintar, pintar!" and gathering around me in a tight and smelly circle would begin to perform impudent monkey tricks to plague me. They stuck their dirty fingers into the soft paint on the palette, made faces at me, stood in my way, assumed childishly indecent attitudes and conducted themselves generally like the little hoodlums they were. I didn't dare to slap any of them for fear of reprisals from the old folks who strangely enough paid not the slightest attention either to me or my picture, something very unusual in street painting in other countries, where as a rule, one is a mecca of interest. Chocolate—sweet, gritty and cheap— saved the day here for me, and my wife purchased it in large cakes at a nearby shop and fed bits of the dark brown oozy substance to each little urchin in turn with the result that in a few days I was no longer insulted, browbeaten, and laughed at. On the contrary, my appearance became almost a reverential gathering place for the infant life of the neighborhood, and when a canvas was completed and I rose to go, sweet smiles, gentle good wishes and positive tears of regret for the end of the chocolate dispensation became the order of the day.

It was a difficult departure, in fact, because on sober reflection, these poor little aimless waifs were growing up in an atmosphere of real destitution and privation. What happened to them in the terrible years that followed one does not wish to contemplate. It was a phase of life which with its poverty and meager living conditions contrasted strangely with that of the ladies and gentlemen who came nightly to our hotel from nearby Santander, the big port on the Bay of Biscay. These refined and wealthy people often took dinner (it never was served before ten) and afterwards danced until the wee small hours of the morning. Life for our party became rather strenuous: not much sleep, plenty of mosquitos, and rich greasy food all contributed to a general feeling of lassitude when breakfast was announced in the morning.

Shortly my own family and myself were to begin

the long trek back to Les Eyzies, while the others left us at Hendaye on their way to see the two extraordinary caves of Tuc d'Audoubert and Les Trois Frères on Count Bégouen's estate in Ariège. From time to time we heard from our friends who had gone to Southern France on their special mission, and when that was accomplished they too returned to Paris to prepare for our further stops on the way to the big Anthropological Congress held that year in Amsterdam.

In the interval of several weeks while resting a bit, the writer painted a small full-length figure of the Abbé standing in his khaki cave suit, carrying his cane and acetylene lamp, smiling at us from a grotto entrance as we had seen him do so often in the weeks just passed. While posing (and I cannot claim that the Abbé was anything but a very casual model) we talked of many things, and I was to get a much clearer insight into the mind of this extraordinary man. We never discussed religion, but on the other hand I found him splendidly informed on many vital matters dealing with world economy, and an enthusiast in his difficult but entirely fascinating line of scientific research.

As the time drew near for our departure for Amsterdam, Henry Field and ourselves were the first to leave Paris, going to Neufchâtel on the Lake of Bienne in Switzerland. There we were to meet

Mr. Vouga, head of the local museum and an expert
on the lives and relics of the Swiss Lake dwellers,
whose story has been so graphically told by the remains found in the shallow waters of various lakes
in that little country and other parts of Europe and
the British Isles. These men, modern as far as their
physical attributes were concerned, must have lived
for centuries in the pile-supported dwellings of their
watery environment. From what we can glean of
their history, the earliest tribes were peoples still
in the late or Neolithic Stone Age, who polished their
flint knives and hatchets and other utensils in a way
not practiced by the Neanderthal or even the Cro-
Magnon races. Mr. Vouga appeared pleased to see
us. He explained at length the history of the discovery and subsequent intensive study of this interesting civilization. He told us too that since
the advent of the airplane aerial views of the pile
formations had been possible with the revelation that
the great wooden stakes had been driven down into
the lake bottom in certain very definite lines, long
curves or straight sections and not haphazardly as
was at first supposed.

Splendid relics were on view in the museum cases,
bits of horse harness, stone and pottery forms of
every description, weapons, tools, etc., fragments of
woven cloth, fish nets, hooks and harpoons, and
scores of other interesting items all indicative of

a high state of civilization not exceeded anywhere else in the world of that day. The Late Stone, the Bronze, and the Iron Ages were all represented, enough in fact to assist the scientists to fairly well picture the situations that must have existed in those ancient eras. Man was evidently very much on the upward trend of his earthly existence. He knew so much about so many things and his astounding ability to make objects of every sort and kind was growing by leaps and bounds. Evidently too he had become a farmer, as evidenced by the skeletons of dogs, cattle, horses, goats, sheep, and pigs discovered among the countless objects retrieved from the lake bottom.

It appears that he had built his huts on piles, close to shore, but that on the land he probably maintained a little farm of domesticated creatures both for their flesh and milk, and skins which were made into clothing. This aggregation of domesticated creatures was a revelation to the scientific world. It really was a milestone in man's future history. For now he was obliged to remain generally in one place during his lifetime. The homestead and its responsibilities tied him to a fairly static condition of living and enabled him to vastly increase his productive powers in the way of home comforts, assured food supply, and permanent dwellings for himself and his numerous family. Many of the settlements had been at some time or other destroyed by fire set either by enemies or accidentally started by members of the community. At any rate, the very element which destroyed these airy dwellings served also to protect by a coat of carbon numerous articles of household use which otherwise might have disintegrated during their long immersion in the cold water of the lake. Everything naturally fell finally into the silt of the lake bottom, there to rest for ages until modern man succeeded in raising them again to the surface and with much care and labor preserved them in the local museum. We have referred at greater length to these enlightening civilizations which flourished for so long in the story of man's earlier development.

From Neufchâtel we went to Heidelberg, picturesque university town, and gazed with interest at the veritable so-called Mauer jaw, a great and beautifully preserved specimen complete with teeth, which as already stated had been dug up in a gravel pit not far from Munich. Then on to Amsterdam by train through Cologne and along the picturesque curves of the Rhine. Amsterdam, cool, expensive, but for a couple of weeks the center of interest for world anthropologists, gave us all a truly royal welcome. The Prince Regent, husband of Queen Wilhelmina, entertained the assembled scientists with an elaborate dinner at the great Krasnapolski Restaurant,

where we ate and drank with gusto and listened to
an address from the Regent himself, along with
the scientific discussions by celebrated men from the
four corners of the globe—all gathered to discuss
with each other the latest finds in the tremendous
history of ancient man.

A special scientific treat was the trip to Haarlem
to hear Professor Dubois discuss his wonderful find
in 1891 of the skullcap and femur of a very primitive manlike being which he had named *Pithecanthropus erectus*. Later at the end of his discourse
he showed for the first time in public these priceless
relics of an ancient type of humanity which had
lived perhaps 300,000 years ago in the forests of
Java, and which indicated furthermore a closer
affinity with the great primates than had ever been
realized by the savants of the day. It was an impressive sight, the interior of that small room in Haarlem
filled to suffocation with world experts on the subject who now for the first time were looking at the
actual bones of the extremely ancient fossil while they
listened intently to Dubois' description of it, and how
and where it was discovered on the large tropical
island. This was really a memorable occasion and one
not to be forgotten because of its extreme significance
to science in general. The meeting was not all technical, however, for we made trips to Maarken and
visited the splendid collections of the Ryks Museum,

where the ever memorable canvas of Rembrandt's "Night Watch" glowed in a richly brilliant and wonderful manner, one of the world's great master-pieces, but one which almost killed Rembrandt's prestige as a painter, for the paltry reason that he had refused to bring out with equal strength and prominence each one of the figures represented. Apparently human nature changes very little through the centuries because the master practically starved to death for want of the meager sum which might have helped to keep him in good health and spirits until the end of a superbly artistic career.

A number of very prominent men in the field of anthropology contributed interesting papers on the subject during the course of this meeting: Sir Arthur Keith, Sir Grafton Elliot-Smith, M. Pittard from Geneva, the Abbé, of course, Count Bégouen, Dr. Absolon from Czechoslovakia, and scores of others, all interesting, well informed and experts upon their particular subject. We just sat back and drank it all in with satisfaction and much intellectual profit. We had covered a good deal of country since the day when we had left Paris for Les Eyzies, but the memory of that trip will always remain a bright spot in a world darkened today by the shadow of impending trouble. In addition it gave us, as nothing else could, a general understanding of the whole great subject of prehistoric man and his develop-

ment and culture through long years of evolution
from an apelike being to the splendid stature of
the Cro-Magnon man, at which period he had sprung
forth with the renewed energy of a superior mental
activity to seize and make his own a vast series of
accomplishments hitherto undreamed of in all the
history of creation.

APOTHEOSIS OF THE
BRONZE AGE

The glow of advancing day is streaming far into
the heavens as the clouds of obscurity roll back from
the crowded years of man's tremendous advance
into the forefront of intellectual achievement. Two
rugged forms loom high upon the rocks above the
wave crests of a northern ocean—each cloaked figure
holding in his sinewy hands a long curved horn of
bronze, the *Lurs* of an ancient Danish folk. Superb
musical instruments these, used only upon solemn
and ritualistic occasions. In ever-increasing glory
the arrows of the sun god strike like flame against
the stalwart trumpeters as they blow a soft deep
note, a farewell salute to the Old Bronze Age now
fast drawing to its close. What supreme effort is
expressed in the sonorous brazen voices, what times
of disappointment, fear, and death amidst the

shadows of a primeval world! Slowly the long res-
onant tones die away, rising again in a refrain of
cheer and encouragement to the hardy adventurers
in the dragon boat beneath the foam-lashed cliff.
Standing in the vessel's prow, the spirit of mankind
faces with hands upraised the brilliance of a new
life of thought and experience. Willing arms strike
the paddles deep into the blue seas of knowledge and
the lusty crew, symbolic of man's courage and tenacity, urge the ship forward as destiny's fateful
hand guides her plunging full into the golden light
of recorded history.

ANCIENT MAN IN AMERICA

To most of us, as citizens of a great democracy,
the superlative is a perfectly natural measure of our
state of mind. We live in a tremendous country,
accumulate vast wealth, raise the biggest crops,
have the greatest mechanical output, the finest rail-
roads, and numbers of other extraordinary and awe-
inspiring things to talk about and of which we are
naturally proud. We are interested too in prehistoric
man and all his works, but unfortunately we haven't
as yet been able to discover the bones of any *very*
ancient human beings on this continent. It isn't the
lack of intense interest nor the begrudging of a lot

of hard work that have thus far frustrated our efforts in this direction, but simply that for some reason, *really* primitive man never seems to have set foot upon our shores.

This important yet discouraging fact has been so often expressed in no uncertain terms by our ablest anthropologists that we would think the statement might have had some effect upon the great mass of our people. Nevertheless, and in spite of this dictum, the patriotic American goes right on excavating the skeletons and skulls of our ancient Indian inhabitants, feeling assured that in his particular case the statement couldn't possibly be true. As a result of this highly resistant state of mind, we read with interest and amusement the heated discussions between excavator and scientist over just who was who in America and speculations as to when the latest exhumed individual actually lived and had his being. But scientists are brave men and they stand as Dr. Hooton of Harvard so humorously puts it, "like Horatius at the Bridge." In this case, the region of the old Alaskan bridge between Asia and America allowed only comparatively recent human beings (old-time Mongoloid people, but related to our present-day Indians) to pass that fateful way. Anything earlier, any man with truly primitive characteristics such as an individual of the old Neanderthal species, never did at any time reach this land of promise.

It's a bitter disappointment, of course, but if such invasions were or could have been the case, no class of individuals would be so deeply and enthusiastically interested as the scientists themselves. For let us remember, this is not a *new* country by any means, though often referred to as such in our histories. On the contrary, many parts of it are exceedingly old, more ancient in fact than most known regions of the earth's surface.

The Hudson Bay country, for example, (geologically speaking the so-called *Canadian Shield*) goes back to the very beginning of land exposures, a matter of several hundred million years. Nova Scotia, the Catskills and the Adirondack Mountains are also hoary with the ages through which they have passed, while many other places particularly in eastern North America are stamped with the brand of a most respectable antiquity. Thus as far as age goes, the great continent might easily have been a perfect home for the very earliest of the human type of mammal, yet it appears this was not to be, for as we know, our primal cradle was either in Asia or Africa, and the two vast continents of North and South America did not see any specimen of *Homo sapiens* until he had advanced far upon the road of his truly manlike qualities. We shall have to be content with the spectacle of some Asiatic clans, grown restless in their own vast environment, setting

out perhaps 20,000 years ago across the then continuous land area between eastern Asia and Alaska,
and gradually spreading over the tremendous spaces
of their new home until in the course of time they
had occupied, though sparsely, most of both North
and South America.

These first nomads brought with them certain cultural objects, stone implements, spears, spear throwers, a little basketry perhaps, and a domesticated
dog of some variety. Where the parent stock of that
strange little canine brute came from is still a mystery
just as the dog which often figures in the relics of
the Swiss Lake Dwellers successfully conceals his
wild origin. But no doubt the dog was as always a
great help in tracking down and holding large game
animals until they could be killed by the hunters.

Gradually these early settlers separated, some
electing to remain near the place of their first landing; others, more adventurous, beginning long journeys to the north along the Arctic Ocean; others went
south along the Pacific coast, while still larger numbers penetrated the vast forests, or roved about over
the plains, until they eventually reached the eastern
edges of the continent. Later, there were migrations
southward into what are now our southern states;
then still further south into Mexico and the Isthmus.
At long last man, always of a definite Indian type,
succeeded in populating many parts of South Amer-

ica. Thus we see him today existing as far south as the very tip of that immense continent.

In North America, owing to the great size of the country, living conditions for these hardy invaders differed much in character, governed naturally by their geographic situation. Food problems varied immensely, and different kinds of game animals required special methods of hunting and capture. Thus we see the northern tribes along the Arctic Ocean as fishermen and hunters of sea-living animals, whales, seals, otters, etc., much after the manner of the modern Eskimo. South of the region lay a vast cold section of the country where great herds of caribou (practically the same as the European reindeer) grazed and furnished food for these races of men. Below this lay the great open plains supporting monstrous herds of bison, huge brutes with thickly furred heads and bodies, and at the same time not difficult to kill. Gradually certain tribes resolved themselves into the so-called plains Indians, while branches of this stock wandering ever eastward were to be known as the eastern tribes of the red man family—the types discovered by our forefathers when they landed from the Dutch, Spanish, English, and French ships.

On the lower west coast strangely primitive tribes existed. In fact, a few members of these old stocks are still living in the mountains of California in much the same way as did their ancestors thousands of years ago. These people have nothing except a few rude tools; they make fine baskets and subsist on acorns and a few other vegetable substances, a diet eked out perhaps by an occasional find of birds' eggs, a lizard or two, or some small animal which they contrive to snare or capture by stealth. All in all, these modern representatives of the old migrations are a degenerating lot and will disappear completely within a few years. There were many other tribes and races of the Mongoloid peoples arriving in America from Asia and some of them probably did not appear until during comparatively late periods in American prehistory.

In time, however, certain rather more definite divisions of these older tribes begin to be apparent in various parts of the continent. Some of them, who lived all through the east central portions of the country, we know as the Mound Builders, and there were and are today the agricultural types such as the modern Pueblos, who lived in villages and cultivated the soil. Corn, most valuable of all their crops, was developed from a wild grass (*Teocentli*), and they also had squash, beans, and in certain regions, potatoes.

In what way the great races known as the Toltecs and Aztecs of Mexico, the Mayas of Yucatan, and the Incas of the Andes came into being we do not exactly know, but in these wonderful peoples lay some unique seed of cultural development surpassing all other American races, and placing them on a par with the great civilized cultures of the far eastern world. Brilliantly endowed by nature with the power to conceive and construct magnificent architectural works, they also possessed an extraordinary aptitude for things religious. So much so that much of their daily living was made up of festivals, rituals, dances, and decorating their temple walls with superb sculptures, reliefs, or murals done in splendid colors and decorative and symbolic designs. Compared with the works of these great tribes, all other Indian activities, with the possible exception of certain great pieces executed by the mound-builders, sink into insignificance. It seems incredible that such a highly developed type of civilization could have arisen in this country without any apparent contacts with other parts of the world. Their art is amazing in its scope, its variety, and splendidly artistic results, and their languages and scientific studies, developed also to a high degree of excellence, seem part and parcel of a type of intellectual superiority of the very highest order. There was, however, a core of fanatical cruelty in these people as attested by some of their religious rites; and they loved the pomp and luxury of sumptuous surroundings, fine fabrics, resplendent bird plumes for their headdresses, and magnificent gold ornaments with which to adorn themselves upon festal occasions.

Unfortunately, they were not alone in their love of the precious gleaming metal, so that when the early Spanish conquerors landed, their advent spelled the doom of these magnificent peoples. Never had the greedy Spaniards seen so much gold nor any so easy to acquire. Forthwith the campaign of ruthless destruction began and the natives were no match for men in steel armor who carried guns loaded with powder and ball. The strangers also rode horses, great beasts new to the Indians who fled incontinently before these terrible creatures and the fierce and still more terrible men upon their backs. It took time, of course, thus to practically annihilate these entrenched and cultivated races, but the Spaniards showed no mercy. They slew and captured hundreds of the frightened aborigines, robbed them of their treasures, and burnt and pillaged to their hearts' content. Slowly the Indians were overcome, their magnificent edifices crumbled into the primeval forests, and the glorious empires of these inspired early Americans had come to a terrible and unnecessary end. The events here chronicled are of course not those of great antiquity, having occurred but a few hundred years ago. Nevertheless, the *origins* of the races themselves take us well back into the distant past where they vanish into the usual gloom of prehistory.

The great tribes designated in a general way as mound builders are also only vaguely known except by their extraordinary constructions in earth, stones, and clay, situated in various central sections of our country. If we may judge by the magnitude and extent of their works, these curious people must have been very numerous in prehistoric days. The purpose of the mounds is not always clear, though some were definitely used as burial chambers. Others, however, like the Great Serpent Mound in Adams County, Ohio, appears to be a purely symbolic monument of vast dimensions. Situated on a bluff above a creek bed, the great coils lie along the ground in graceful curves for over 1000 feet and terminate in a beautifully fashioned spiral tail. The head, with what appears to be an egg in its open jaws, is also a most cleverly fashioned bit of earthwork construction. The great serpent, unique among all the monuments of prehistory, is fortunately preserved as a public possession.

We have already referred to the controversies growing out of the average American's determination to find and recover from his earth some manlike creature from extreme antiquity who has never been discovered upon this continent. Nevertheless, man's early appearance in this country has now been set back much further in history than was originally thought possible because of comparatively new discoveries, the first in 1926, with many others since that time. In that year a band of excavators under the direction of J. D. Figgins, then director of the Colorado Museum of Natural History at Denver, uncovered a series of bison bones near the little town of Folsom, New Mexico. These bones belonged to a very large bison, an animal with a huge hump over the shoulder region, and an altogether magnificent type of the bovine race extinct for perhaps 20,000 years. In digging up the remains, pieces of flint were also observed, and later a flint arrow or spear point of a peculiar shape came to light. Mr. Figgins was overjoyed because he was quite sure that something new in the history of early man in our country was being divulged for the scientists' edification. A very few of his confreres rejected this viewpoint, assuming that the juxtaposition of the arrow points with the old skeleton was purely accidental and that they were probably of comparatively recent Indian manufacture. This decision did not satisfy the museum director who kept on with the excavation work until all his brother scientists were compelled to admit the flints really belonged to the period of the bison bones, especially when one was found practically embedded between two bison ribs.

Although excavated in a rather unspectacular manner, there are several very interesting aspects to his really important piece of paleontological evidence of man's greater antiquity in North America. In the first place the discovery clears the way for a further survey of a very interesting subject, as it calls attention to the necessity of analyzing more thoroughly the association of man with types of fossil animals thought to have become extinct many thousands of years ago. Again the dart or spear points are unique in shape and method of manufacture. In general, they are described as leaf-shaped, but they had also been flaked out in a unique way by a long longitudinal groove or hollow extending from the base of the point almost to the tip. Sometimes this groove occurred only on one side of the point, in others both sides were involved. The name *Folsom Point,* given because the artifact was first discovered in the vicinity of Folsom, New Mexico, is now a fixed type and has since been found in other parts of the country, thus proving that an extremely ancient race of people was spread over large areas of the continent a very long time ago. It must be said that science owes a great deal to the interested layman in the furtherance of many of these studies of ancient man in America, especially to local farmers and ranchers living in regions where such finds are possible. These shrewd and observant individuals have often been able to give valuable information to parties searching for hidden treasure in the shape of bones and artifacts of various kinds.

Furthermore, they all agree that points of the

Folsom (and also what are known as Yuma) type
are usually found more deeply buried than are those
of the later Indian cultures. In other words the men
who made and used the points may have preceded
these more recent tribes of Indian peoples by hundreds or even thousands of years. Were this to be
the case, it presupposes a long history for even our
later Indians, and it does not seem strange that at
the time of America's discovery by old-world adventurers certain tribes and divisions of Indian peoples
were found in such an advanced state of civilization.
Certainly Cortez and Pizarro had reason to be
amazed at the perfected cultures which flourished
so magnificently in the regions of their conquests. But
this same high culture was apparently little in evidence when Columbus first saw the red men of San
Salvador, or even much later, at the time of the
English, Dutch, and French explorers' first visits
here. These northern Indians were undoubtedly
splendid specimens of savagery, although culturally
they were still in the stone age of human development, living in huts or tents, and making their weapons and other utensils of flint, bone, ivory, wood,
and other substances. In fact, although the use of
copper in a natural state was known to some of our
Indian peoples, no actual bronze or iron age discoveries have ever been recorded in this country, with
the exception, of course, of certain Norse relics.

However, the Indian, as a man was, we must admit, the equal physically of any European type, ancient or otherwise. Especially has this been true of the plains and eastern seaboard tribes. Mentally we may picture them as exceedingly acute, quick to learn from and take advantage of the greed and duplicity of the white man, matching their wits with his, and very often coming off victorious in the encounter. How clever had been our earliest human immigrants from Siberian shores we do not know, but we may infer a comparatively high mental and physical combination which enabled these venturesome nomads to take up their abode here in full possession of all the necessary faculties for extracting a living from their immediate environment.

The long-cherished myth of the *extreme* antiquity of man in the Americas must in all probability be relegated to the background of scientific research, but it in no way lessens the tremendous value of the story that a sufficiently ancient civilization did once spread through the two continents. In its larger sense, the American era of prehistory plays an important part in the allover picture of humanity from its earliest inception (hundreds of thousands of years ago) up to the later phases of Cro-Magnon occupation, and still more developed types in the Bronze and Iron Ages in Europe. Especially is this so because of the fact that, as we know, Indian culture

for the most part was, when first encountered, still in
a stage no longer visible in the old-world scene—a
type of quasi-civilization which ceased to exist there
after the days of the earlier Swiss Lake Dwellers.
For convenience, several great epochs and races or
cultures have been tabulated in both the North and
South American continents, and some of these have
been referred to here; but it is not our purpose to
discuss such undoubtedly interesting subjects because
they are somewhat out of our province and have been
most carefully elucidated by highly trained specialists.

To what degree the Aztec and Mayan civilizations might have developed had they not been ruth-
lessly destroyed is naturally a matter of speculation,
particularly because they had advanced so far along
the higher roads of learning that it seemed possible
for them to have really taken a place in contemporaneous European world affairs. This might not have
been the case, however, owing to the fierce and
unleashed passions of their so-called civilized discov-
erers from across the sea, where stormy events and
dark and sinister influences were at work in the Christian lands of Europe and the near East. The important fact to remember in this connection is that the
two civilizations, developed under widely different
conditions, clashed at every point, and that the elimi-
nation of one was inevitable. Also, there is the interesting thought that, presupposing that our earliest

ancestor actually came from Mongoloid relatives, his further development into the red man of the western world indicates a very different type of ancestor from that of the European races. In other words, his ancestors and ours in very early days must not have belonged to the same racial stock. That being the case, it raises the query as to when and where Mongol and white men separated from one another in certain of their physical characteristics. Possibly we detect here a corroboration of the theory of a multiple ancestry for man, each living under different conditions and showing very early racial differences.

The two basic regions at present regarded as possible sites for man's ancestral home are, as we know, South Africa and some rather vague sections of the Asiatic continent. Yet the very great antiquity of these sites and the primitive characteristics of such creatures as *Plesianthropus,* the South African ape man, and even old *Pithecanthropus* of the Javan region preclude any very definite conclusions on these points. It is quite impossible to say from an examination of such ancient relics into what special type of recent men they might finally have developed. They seem far too generalized in form to permit close comparison between them and *Homo sapiens.* By recent we mean, of course, the early historic and later European types, people of our own general physiognomy who had made their first appearance in Europe and the near East. Yet the fact that our earliest American is of the Mongoloid persuasion does throw perhaps a bit of light upon the subject. Naturally, his Asiatic predecessors must have been also of the Mongol breed, but how ancient is their lineage we have no means of knowing. The fact that Peking man is an Asiatic will not help us greatly here because he again had not yet advanced towards a strictly human form sufficiently to enable us to compare him with the Mongolian races of today. At any rate our old Bering Strait land-bridge travelers very definitely aid us in checking a possible 20,000-year-old yellow man as he set foot for the first time upon the beaches of the New World.

His coming, and the utensils which he brought with him—the forms of which he was subsequently to improve and increase—inform us of yet another very interesting phase of man's development. It is always a controversial matter of interest to anthropologists that human beings of very different and widely separated environments should show marked similarity both in the methods of making and the substances used for their various tools, weapons, and other objects of daily use. Consistently, they evidence the strange phenomenon of what we might call parallel cultures. Fortunately, the intriguing history of ancient man in the Americas is a most striking example of that peculiarity for the reason that we have now had here for thousands of years a type of being whose activities strongly resembled foreign cultures, though not directly influenced by them. Although isolated for a very long period, the Indian has acquired similar arts of basket and pottery making, weaving, the use of beaten copper in its natural state, and (in the resplendent Mayan and Aztec civilizations) a facility of hand and eye as well as an understanding of architectural construction quite beyond our comprehension. It may be said, however, that in general the American culture lagged far behind that of Europe during a 20,000-year period of development, for our old-world ancestors had in a similar interval of time advanced from the Cro-Magnon stage of learning through a vastly improved type of existence right up to the period of iron, gunpowder, shipping, and endless other activities of a highly sophisticated civilization. Whatever ideas of false grandeur may be found in the white man's cosmos, the extraordinary story of his comparatively recent past is enough to justify at least some of the more sober evaluations of his conduct and achievements since the era of the New Stone Age.

It has been suggested that no strictly great advance culturally is possible among human beings without the stimulus and the competition of adjacent civilizations. Dr. Fay Cooper Cole of Chicago voices this idea when he says that the Cro-Magnon people of Europe, though physically and artistically superior, did not advance in other ways because of that lack of competitive stimuli. In any case, the tribes which followed the Cro-Magnon era had plenty of this kind of mental incentive and they certainly uphold the professor's thesis to a remarkable degree. While we in America know of the existence of a long series of tribes and cultures extending over thousands of years, presumably these tribes were all derived from the original Asiatic stock. Although they enlarged and improved their general efficiency, their type of living was on a comparatively low scale, with the exception of the Maya, Aztec, and Inca peoples. This may be true, but a survey of American prehistory will disclose with what a vast amount of energy these peoples were endowed and how cleverly and bravely they were able to overcome difficulties and exist in many different environments throughout the stupendous areas of the two Americas.

Surely one may marvel at man's adaptability under any and all conditions of temperature, altitude, and general food supply; how he met and conquered every obstacle to his advance in any desired direction, and by the exercise of extreme sagacity, ingenuity, and an indomitable will, existed here for thousands of years. It's a long way from the Arctic Circle to Patagonia, yet our aborigines accomplished the traversing of that distance under anything but ideal conditions. To do so our Indian predecessors used every ounce of their physical strength and endurance, their acute sense of general direction, and their uncanny abilities in the procuring of food of every sort and kind. It is small wonder that American youth is thrilled by the story of the Indian and that the red man's adventures make so deep an impression upon the minds and even the characters of certain white adults whose instinct for and love of the great open spaces seems almost on a par with that of their red-skinned predecessors.

The astonishing variety of materials used, and the high standard of the artistic results achieved by ancient and recent Indian peoples, are always a source of satisfaction to anyone deeply interested in these manifestations of human skill and high mental organization. Perhaps no other early human type has so clearly demonstrated man's superiority over materials in an almost unlimited variety of artistic productions concerned with the more mystical side of their lives as well as other and more prosaic activities. From the early days of human occupation, we have implements of stone, both chipped and polished, and not much else in the way of living utensils. Very probably, however, as is the case with European early man, articles of wood have simply disintegrated in the course of time and been destroyed completely. Later in American history, came the bone harpoons of the northern sections of the Mongolian tribes settling along the Arctic Ocean.

These people also made fur garments and may have used dogs to draw their sleds much as do the Eskimos today. They must have been then as now independent of the rest of the world, living as do the polar bears and seals and wolves as a part of nature's many-sided economy. Other tribes to the south and indeed all through the snowy regions of North America invented the snowshoe, a complicated and beautifully made object of extreme value in the deep snows of a northern winter. Many races were caribou hunters, practically dependent not alone for food upon the vast herds of these splendid deer, but for everything else they needed in the way of clothing as well as the bone and horn so necessary for the manufacture of spears, darts, knives, scrapers. In fact, any number of absolutely necessary utensils for daily use in their living camps and on their hunting trips were derived from caribou products.

Further afield, indeed in every part of the great country, the story is repeated, varying in the details but always essentially the same. Man must live, and as an animal he must eat, sleep, and protect himself as much as possible from the weather. In no two other continents of the world could he have found better opportunity for the displaying of all those amazing traits of versatility, adaptability, and courage for which he is so justly celebrated. From the snows of the Arctic to the steaming jungles of South America, the hot plains and deserts of our western country, the savannahs of Florida, and the chilly wastes of Patagonia, man's tremendous resiliency has enabled him to make a home, to have children, and to carry on his necessary life activities in a practical and eminently intelligent way. When we reflect that *one* specific type of the human species, in this case the Indian, has been thus able to accommodate himself to such a vast range of diversified environments, the results are truly astonishing. He has, under varying conditions, proved himself a hunter, a fisherman, an agriculturist, a boat builder, potter, weaver, and architect. In other words, as a full-fledged, capable example of one branch of the Mongoloid race, he seems to have been able to develop in the vast reaches of the Western Hemisphere.

Though reference has been made only casually to the mystical side of the red man's personality, his extraordinary potentialities in this direction are a matter of extreme interest to all students of the subject. In general, all the different branches of the Indian peoples believed in a higher being, all-powerful, and living somewhere in the sky above our verdant earth. They also, as did many other early world peoples, invested natural objects and phenomena with spiritual and mystical properties and

powers. The sun, moon and stars, comets and the
aurora, together with their varying phases and movements, interested them immensely, and upon earth,
all weather changes and what they foretold were
matters of intense and protracted study. Animal life
in general they naturally observed and understood
to a remarkable degree, and certain types of creature,
the bear, the wolf, the fox, and mountain lion, all
carnivora, were objects to be feared and avoided.
The wolverine, or glutton, came in for his share of
attention on account of his seemingly demoniacal
propensities in the destruction of food caches and
articles of clothing, while the beaver was distinctly
an object of veneration because of his clever and
industrious manner of living. Presumably, all earthly
life and everything which could be observed in
the heavens held great and lasting fascination for
the red man, who incorporated these natural objects
into his world of mystical beings, investing each with
some good or evil propensities whose manifold workings might in some way react upon his own existence
either here or in the hereafter.

While not in most cases idol worshipers in the
ordinary sense, they were nevertheless believers in
the value of fetishes, charms, and other objects endowed with fearsomely mystical properties, and the
medicine men of the various tribes made great use
of such things. Especially among the Indians of our

southwestern states, the agricultural section of Indian life, the value of the propitiatory dances, festivals, and other observances to invoke rain for the crops, and to ensure their fullness, was of prime importance. While these rituals remain in force to the present day, they are known to be of great antiquity though perhaps not always conducted under the same conditions. They exemplify, however, by their frequency, variety, and exact attention to form the important part that they play in the lives of many of our Indian tribes. As has been said, no other type has better demonstrated man's insatiable desire for happiness, prosperity, and plenty, and the continuation of life in the hereafter than the red man of the New World, yet he is merely following a pattern inherent in every section of the human race since time immemorial.

We have in the course of this writing cited many different world eras with the appropriate human types which science has allotted to each period. It must seem apparent, however, even to the casual reader, that only one grand and universal family has been under discussion even though many branches of the main tree have flourished and withered in the succession of the ages. Among these the red Indian of the Americas occupies a high place in prehistory from the time of his first entry here and during and after the retreat of the glacial ice some 20,000 years ago.

Death of a titan

Rio Bec. B.: a restoration of a Maya temple

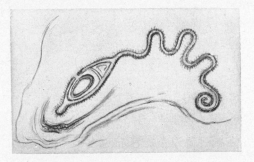

The great Serpent Mound in Adams County, Ohio: relic of the
Mound Builders

HELMUT DE TERRA DISCOVERS MAN SKELETON

The fossilized bones of animals buried at times quite deeply in surface soil or actually exposed by weathering have intrigued man's imagination since the long-distant days of his primitive past. According to the extent of his knowledge at the time of such a discovery, man ascribed many different reasons to their presence in localities scattered throughout the world. It is certain that our earlier ancestors regarded these relics with mingled feelings of awe and curiosity, and very probably did not associate them with anything that had once existed, merely delighting in their singular forms and potential usefulness as spear or arrow points, clubs and hammers, or as ornaments. The collecting of fossils in our own day has become so advanced in its methods that we might almost refer to it as an art to be learned only with great difficulty and after long years of experience in the field. Naturally, certain men excel in this line of scientific research where physical endurance, geological knowledge, and extreme patience are all of prime importance in a successful endeavor to locate and properly excavate some rare and perhaps extremely fragile skeleton of a creature dead for thousands or even millions of years.

As a rule, the expeditions are governed by the special requirements or qualifications of the experts in charge of the work. Some of these men seek only for fossil mammals, others inspect great areas in search of reptile bones or invertebrate specimens, and still another lot, the anthropologists, devote their energies to the unearthing of man's remains. We may be sure, however, that whatever type of creature is being sought for, the work will be hard, the discomforts many, and the rewards of so much labor not always forthcoming, or very disappointing in the total results. When in certain rare cases the much-prized bones of an extinct creature are exposed upon the surface of the soil, or have been partially eroded from the side of a rocky cliff, the find may after all be very fragmentary, badly weathered or otherwise partially destroyed, and the successful recovery of the fossil may still entail a tremendous amount of hard work. But the problem of locating a *buried* specimen of any long-dead creature is an even more difficult task, especially when one actually sets out to find something never before discovered in the vicinity, and conducts the search purely from inference aided by a trained imagination.

How would one go about this vague but fascinating bit of exploration? Dr. Helmut De Terra, an anthropologist of note, has answered that question in a most original and interesting manner. He found what he was looking for by the use of an electrical divining instrument. In December, 1945, De Terra was standing on the shore of an ancient lake bed, now shrunken to a tiny stream, but which even in Cortez's day covered practically the whole valley of Mexico. He had previously explored this region and had learned of the discovery of numbers of very large mammoth bones. Evidently when these great beasts had died their remains had sunk into the swampy edges of what was then a large lake. Either this mammoth had perished from exhaustion and starvation or quite possibly from the spear and arrow wounds resulting from attacks of some race of hitherto undiscovered man. It was this ancient man that De Terra now sought and he had very carefully figured that mechanical instruments might be of help in his strange man-hunt. When first the idea had become a sort of *idée fixe* in the expert's mind, he had considered using a mine-detector device, a war invention for ferreting out hidden land mines secreted just beneath the ground surface and terribly lethal in their effects upon marching troops. But Dr. Hans Lundberg, a Canadian geophysicist, suggested a different electrical contraption as being better suited for this special kind of work. So it happened that Dr. De Terra, assisted by Mexican specialists, began his electrical bloodhound hunt for a possible ancient American who had been dead for perhaps

15,000 years. The search was amazingly successful because the enthusiastic collectors actually located a limited region wherein the electrical indicator was strangely deflected. They dug carefully into three small pits; and on the second day luck was with the scientists, for there, lying upon his face, was the almost complete skeleton of some type of very ancient man. They lifted him with the greatest of care, gazing finally at the features of an Indian, but this red man had distinctly Mongoloid characteristics and his still more ancient ancestors might have walked across the ancient land bridge that once connected Asia and North America. The electrical bloodhound had proved its worth, for never before in all history had a buried skeleton thus been tracked down to its last resting place.

Naturally, De Terra and his Mexican friends rejoiced at this dramatic turn of events, but the scientist went further in his studies. He wished to prove that perhaps this type of prehistoric man had been present at the death of one or more of those huge mammoths whose great bones were known to exist at no great distance from the man skeleton. Again he was successful, not by employing electrical energy, but by employing the trained human eye in a careful survey of the region. When bones of a great mired mammoth were unearthed, with suggestive knifelike cuts upon its surface, he was convinced that here at last was what he had so long been seeking, concrete evidence of the attempted destruction of a gigantic pachyderm by early Mexican hunters.

We may reconstruct this tragic scene with our newly acquired knowledge to help us. The blue of a subtropical sky is reflected in the glistening surface of the big lake, and herds of huge mammoths with magnificent curling tusks are feeding and drinking along its marshy shores. Suddenly there is excitement in the herd, fierce, wild trumpetings and a stampede of mighty bodies away from the treacherous lake edge where one of their number has become mired in the sticky, tenacious muck. The lone victim is dazed for a moment, not fully realizing his predicament. Then wildly surging backward and forward, trunk upraised and ivory tusks flashing, he exerts every ounce of his stupendous strength to free himself from the dreaded quicksand in which one leg is now deeply submerged. These titanic struggles avail him nothing except that he sinks still deeper into the mire. Again he rears, the vast limbs tensed to the last degree, trumpeting now in crescendo blasts of terror and desperation. The noise and confusion are terrific, increasing as a horde of armed savages suddenly appear, hurling their spears and shooting arrows into the quivering body of the almost exhausted creature. While not able to kill the huge beast with their puny weapons, the very near presence of man is sufficient to drive any wild creature to distraction, especially under the terrible stress of immobility. The gargantuan struggles grow steadily weaker, and in a short time the massive bulk of the dying titan falls slowly to one side, amid a rain of missiles hurled by the exultant savages half crazed with excitement over the prospect of a square meal, perhaps a rarity in their daily living.

The finding of mammoth bones in conjunction with manmade weapons was not unique in North America, but Dr. De Terra's early man is the first to be unearthed in the subtropical regions of this hemisphere. The mammoth (*Imperator*) belongs to the largest and finest species known; a gigantic elephant standing some fourteen feet at the shoulder and bearing tusks sixteen feet along the outer curve. The Mexican man, De Terra's prize, is less spectacular; fairly tall —about 5 feet, 8 inches in height—with a Mongoloid type of features, heavy brow ridges, broad cheeks, and a round head. He is *not* an early type of humanity; merely a member of a very old Indian race. Looking back upon those distant ages we picture both men and many species of animals emigrating from Asia across the Bering Strait into vast new regions never before occupied by members of the human race. Thus arose our first Indian cultures, the subsequent development of many tribes and races of

the red men, and their eventual occupation of the
two Americas.

RIO BEC. B.,
THE LOST MAYA TEMPLE

For a thousand years the verdure of a tropical
forest had cast its shadow upon the crumbling walls
of this Maya temple, hidden deep within the heart
of Yucatan. A thousand years when perhaps no
human eye glimpsed its massive vine-covered stones;
when only bats and birds and creeping things explored the inner recesses of its sacred chambers or
mounted the steep steps that led to the abode of the
gods in its huge corner towers. Then quite suddenly
on Easter Sunday in 1912, the silence of this eerie
spot was broken by the ring of axes and the swish
of machetes. Trees toppled slowly from their lofty
perches on the mass of rubble and fallen façades,
creepers were torn aside and underbrush cleared
from around the base of the beautiful structure. Two
archaeologists, Drs. R. E. Merwin and Clarence L.
Hay, leaders of the Harvard Peabody Museum ex-
pedition, with a corps of helpers, were the moving
spirits of that epic disturbance. They had encountered great difficulties in their search for a series of
long-hidden ruins of an ancient city reported in 1908.

by a French archaeologist, Comte Maurice de
Périgny. Then for a few weeks much happened in
this lonely spot. Photographs and measurements
were made of the building, now partially fallen into
decay, but with a considerable amount of the main
structure standing once again in the bright sunlight,
its twin towers rising for more than fifty feet into
the tropical sky.

Here was a treasure indeed for the intrepid scientists, when discomforts were for the time being forgotten, and an energetic and very careful study made
of this little gem which they called Rio Bec. B., because the Frenchman Périgny had named the nearby
ruins, Rio Bec. A—a prosaic title and merely a
designation of what was perhaps one of the most
beautiful temples ever discovered in the Yucatan
country. Probably constructed between 600 and 700
A.D., it represented a highly developed period of
Mayan architecture and was therefore doubly precious in the eyes of the scientific fraternity. Furthermore, it, together with all the other superb artworks
conceived by the Mayan, Aztec, Toltec, and Inca
cultures, demonstrated the former presence of a most
extraordinary type of new world civilization. The
extent to which these various peoples had advanced
before their careers were rudely interrupted by the
advent of the Spanish conquerors was almost unbe-
lievable. Great cities of magnificent proportions,

their façades richly decorated with reliefs of figures, geometric patterns, symbols of writing, conventionalized animal forms, and astronomical signs and dates, lay scattered throughout Mexico, Yucatan, and the Andean highlands, where rare treasures still remain hidden in the dark forests, deep valleys, and the mountain fortresses of these strange lands.

Today, Rio Bec. B. is once again in this undiscovered realm, for when the explorers had finished their work the trees and vines renewed their all-obliterating task of slow destruction. Again the gloom of heavy foliage enshrouds the lovely architecture and neither bright sun nor the soft rays of the moon can penetrate that dim, dense curtain. Only the softly whispering leaves and branches know just where now lies its vanished beauty, for in the words of Dr. Hay, "The jungle is a jealous custodian of its mysteries."

THE PAST AND THE FUTURE

It is not always easy to discern in a study of man's mentality the dividing line between a mystical approach to his various problems, and the higher aspirations of a deeper and more spiritual aspect of his character. Indeed, these attributes are often so intermingled that the story of one blends imperceptibly into that of the other. Nevertheless we see, as human intellect gradually increased in vigor, resourcefulness, and variety, distinct indications of a more elevated scale of religious worship, a condition which necessitated increasing numbers of priests, soothsayers, and wise men to disclose the way to the greater benefits of the higher learning. There have been, no doubt, even in prehistoric times certain individuals (ethical teachers in fact) who have professed intuition regarding what really constituted the requirements of earthly conduct necessary for the achievement of man's immortality. The extreme complexity of this phase of man's nature thus so graphically demonstrated is only a part of a whole series of ramifications connected with the general question of life, death, and immortality. Rites, festivals, formal burials, dances, and a multitude of material, sensual, and idolatrous customs are and have been more or less a part of this tremendous propitiatory attempt to placate the natural forces in the hope that by so doing he may at last find satisfaction and plenty in some future state of gratified ambition.

Today, civilized man is so engrossed in his own vastly elaborated problems and social affairs that he is apt to forget or else take for granted the fact that there are still on earth peoples of extremely primitive cultural achievements, so primitive that they are in many ways living the life of old *Pithecan-*

thropus of the Java forests 300,000 years ago. Between these lowest types and ourselves exist great numbers of partially civilized races, many of whose customs are of the stone-age variety but who, for one reason or another, make use of certain highly sophisticated utensils derived from trade or barter with the modern world.

The twentieth century with all its tremendous affairs of supreme importance to ourselves has up to this time had little more than a casual influence upon these sequestered races. To us they are of tremendous interest as a kind of living revelation of our own probable appearance in the not-too-distant past. In their actions and reactions they also exhibit a singular and unflattering duplication of what we are prone to think of as our superbly developed ethical ideas and procedures. In other words, we haven't changed to any profound extent in many of the deeper basic emotions that have belonged to man since his first inception as a superior type of mammal. Yet this is not all the truth, nor is it the more wonderful or impressive part of the story of man upon this earth. There is an immense amount of satisfaction to be gained by a wide and careful survey of ourselves and our record here. From the first, it is evident that we are dealing with a complicated personality which will bear watching at every phase of its development and that always there is, in contradistinction to the generality of mammals, an over-lying something, a film of mental or shall we say supernatural awareness not found in any other type of living creature.

Even in the latest reports from South Africa, Professor Raymond Dart speaks of finding remains of fire hearths and weapons made by a being of singularly low mentality who even at that early stage must already have graduated from the great ape class into something with profoundly human possibilities. How else are we to account for this very great discrepancy in behavior and intelligence? What strange force or innate capability has been introduced into the mind of this lowly animal? Remember that these events happened, if Professor Dart's time chart is correct, perhaps a million years ago. Yet the great apes of the time, if we read their story accurately, were much like those of today for the very good reason that the recent ape has advanced practically not at all, at least mentally, in those same million years. What can account for that extraordinarily static condition in view of the fact that his subhuman contemporary had long ago reached his present position of extreme proficiency in so many things?

We may ponder these questions to the best of our ability, but the answers are still not known by any human being no matter how expert his judgment and scientific knowledge may be. Of course, we are in danger in this era, as always, of confusing material gain with the absolutely necessary attribute of ethical understanding and conduct. It is not enough to be aware of the latter, we must follow its maxims if we wish for accord, and live as the higher consciousness directs. The constant clash of these two opposing forces in the heart of man is sufficient to account for his dire need to recognize the essential and tremendous difference between the two.

No doubt the desire to acquire and keep what he has secured are both prime characteristics of humanity, derived from his strictly mammalian ancestors, while the evolution of his mentality towards an *ethical* goal is a much later but not so easily understood side of his personality. This latter quality is certainly a digression from the usual course of evolution in any mammal which, though its history may show a gradual increase in general mentality, seems to halt very definitely when a maximum of brain capacity has been attained. In man, the limit of this evolution is not yet in sight, though in what direction further changes may occur is a matter for speculation. What we will eventually become, what future lies in store for us are not in this writer's opinion very important matters.

Far more crucial for our peace of mind here on earth is a more profound comprehension of our present difficulties and a clearer insight into the moving causes of our gathering troubles. We will err if we think that there is anything new in those exhibitions of greed, ferocity, and paltry personal and political aspirations which are a commonplace nowadays in world affairs. To understand better what we are and why we now do things in a certain way, the study of man's unique appearance in a world of teeming animal life, and his subsequent mysterious differentiation from those mammalian relatives, will definitely be of vast assistance in comprehending at least a portion of our long unwritten history. The inheritance and the maintenance of many of our fundamental peculiarities will become evident by this line of investigation, and we will be able, by an awareness of their primeval origin, to regard philosophically many curious and highly objectionable traits in the human animal, which might otherwise seem late developments in our long list of dangerous eccentricities. Certainly in the pages of this book our attention has many times been called to these always latent and deep-seated animal traits in man's character which partially explain many strange and seemingly incomprehensible episodes in his history. These fundamental facts were, of course, long ago recognized by distinguished savants and philosophers, and all ethical teachers have realized the dangers to which man subjected himself when such exhibitions of primitive mammalian propensities were not kept in subjection either by force of arms or by the example of a superior and self-sacrificing code of living.

Yet man is a stubborn and foolish creature, even now a child in many of his thoughts and actions, and he has an inherent dislike of listening to or profiting by the experience of others. He would rather suffer agonies than accept advice, no matter how good or how well intended. It would seem the height of absurdity had we not already been aware of this structure in his character which deliberately throws away a priceless advantage possessed by no other living creature. How men have suffered from this incredibly stupid negation of common sense is an old story to all students of history. There again we must accept the facts as they are, not necessarily as we would like them to be.

For our own better understanding of the nature of man, it is well to remember that he attained his physical peak in the Cro-Magnon eras, perhaps 15,000 years ago, and that little or no advance is discernible in his mental capabilities after the late Egyptian, Greek, and Roman periods of high culture. In most cases, what we have learned materially since those days has been an elaboration and a multiplication of most of the great principles more or less envisioned by the master minds of that time. It is not here a question of whether or not the Greeks had grasped the theory of relativity or understood the principles of the steam engine. The point is that mentally they had advanced to a point where an explanation of the theory, or a similar one, would have been perfectly comprehended and the advantages realized. As we are concerned primarily in these pages with the all-around development of man up to the time of his emergence into the realm of written history, it will not be amiss to go over again in our studies the amazing story of his utterly unique progression upward during the long ages of his adolescent period.

There can be no doubt about the drastic changes which have occurred in his physical construction nor the equally interesting and peculiar enlargement of the skull with its correspondingly greater brain capacity and perfection of mental characteristics. While, as has been said, such changes often are evident in other mammalian stocks, no other creature has displayed the extraordinarily rapid and extensive brain growth which is unique in man. The various drawings showing this remarkable transition from an almost flat-skulled creature with a heavy projecting face to the Cro-Magnon man type with his high upright forehead, great rounded skullcap, and delicate but prominent chin are the best illustration of what really happened to the head shapes of our ancient relatives during a million years of evolution. Within that same skullcap, as its form and brain capacity changed, great things were happening, changes which were to eventually produce a being like ourselves in every way. Had man stopped at this point in his upward growth, the result, while encouraging, would hardly have been more than mildly impressive.

Nature had done her best for this type of creature; great blessings, mental and physical, had been showered upon his tall and handsome personality, and he had been carefully prepared for still greater life adventures. His magnificent upright form enabled him to stand, walk, run, and climb with perfect ease and efficiency, while his mental status was of a high order and he possessed the inestimable ability to see accurately and to record what he saw with skill and precision. He lacked, however, either from constitutional reasons or as a result of his relatively isolated condition, the initiative to progress in practical ways, and we have the picture of this splendid specimen of humanity as he reached a kind of social impasse. This evidently was not the case with the races succeeding him who, as we have pointed out, perhaps advanced from both the northern and eastern regions of Europe and the adjoining Asiatic continent. They had no inhibitions and developed rivalries, wars, local feuds, and more and more highly cultivated industries. In fact, they were much like ourselves in the scope and manner of their activities. In them we see fully accentuated all those disagreeable and lovable traits which are our heritage today.

From that time, we have kept up a continual advance in the production of things useful and beautiful, surrounded ourselves with material wealth of every kind, become masters of astuteness, greed, cunning, and profligacy, and failed miserably to enhance greatly the spiritual side of our inner nature. In vain, successive ethical teachers have preached, admonished, and gravely warned us of the dire consequences of the path we have chosen to follow. Can it be that after all they have wasted their time, their effort, and their lives in showing us the better way to live in amicable and profitable relationship with one another? It is more probable, however, that our so distant forebears, could we but know them more, would have exhibited much the same series of ethically suicidal qualities. Yet for some strange reason they managed to survive, often in the midst of privation, for an immense period of time. Here again our study of ancient man, especially during his almost apelike period of mentality, will tell us that basically all these low and seemingly dangerous traits are simply evidences of man's truly mammalian character and not something entirely new in his personality. We are obliged to realize these facts because science has shown us so conclusively our very close affinity with the simian world, not only in physical construction but in many of our brain reactions as well. To be sure, it is not always expedient to call attention to this very apparent liaison, but we can not ignore it, for in so doing we lose sight of one of the most inspiring thoughts that can come to us in our perusal of man's history—the fact that poor weak creatures as we are, we have yet been able to sever many of the bonds that once held us so firmly to the primeval anthropoid stock. There is comfort and inspiration in that thought, giving us new hope, new courage, and a more rational line of reasoning on the problems of humanity.

If in the past man has been able to at least circumvent the distinctly animal side of his nature by attention to the more elevated ambitions of his intellectual capacity, it should be increasingly simpler as time progresses to forestall and rise above these same propensities. The human race must always, even in its more primitive state, have been more or less aware of the differences between man and his nearest relative, the ape, recognizing his own superiority and taking advantage of it. The code of action for the primate was not that of man primeval even in the infancy of our lowliest ancestors. There must have been an instinctive mental drawing apart of the two types of animal, a gulf between them which has continued to widen through the ages principally because of that uncanny overlay of spiritual and ethical isolation which sets man forever apart from all other created beings. Thus by the scanning of our past history, seeking precedents for what otherwise seem an inscrutable series of reactions in man's cosmos we find ourselves on the only possible road to an understanding of ourselves and our relations to the world in general. Whether or not we choose to avail ourselves of this knowledge will be a matter laid absolutely on man's own doorstep.

Naturally there is another side to the entire subject, and we must not get the idea that all reactions in the conduct of our past relatives are obnoxious, low, and bestial. This attitude on our part would ignore a host of man's more wonderful qualities—his extraordinary persistence, courage, sagacity, and resourcefulness in the face of dangers often too terrible to contemplate, his patience and adaptive possibilities, and his precise skill in the making of complicated objects of every sort. Again, our study of ancient man will show us that early in prehistory our forefathers seemed to possess miraculous powers of producing from natural resources everything they needed for the maintenance of themselves and their progeny. We see this same ability exhibited today among so-called primitive peoples. How they weave fibers to make mats, baskets, nets, thatch for their huts, bowls, weapons, pottery, anything and everything suited to their own needs and requirements, and all so cleverly and expertly accomplished! The sight is a cheering one as it displays for our edification and gratification the outward workings of a mind endowed with the qualities of extreme power of concentration and accurate perception. From the study of our very ancient relatives in South Africa we are amazed to learn that they too knew so much about abstruse natural forces and were even then able to make use of this knowledge for their own benefit. In very truth, man began his conquest of the world at an early date, a thought which should give us renewed courage and satisfaction. It must, however, be realized that in order to understand properly these phases of man's psychology we must accept the idea not only of his dual but even his triple personality, and the strange contradictions for which such a combination may be responsible in his life story.

There is danger, however, in placing too much stress upon the virtues of man's undoubted mechanical abilities, especially among highly civilized peoples. Naturally, no two human beings are exactly alike in all particulars, some excelling in one line, some in another. Herein lies one of the great difficulties of man's existence, a problem of long standing although it was less trying in the days of his earlier and far simpler scale of living. Competition (a word used so frequently in the modern world and a type of activity regarded by many as an absolute necessity for our present-day existence) no doubt holds an important position in our economy, but competition unrestrained can spell only ruin to vast numbers of innocent people whose affairs happen to lie in the path of the contending parties. We are not here entering the lists for any discussion of modern economics, but we are attempting to show that in ancient man, as we raise the curtain upon his thoughts and actions in the long ago, the same living difficulties become at once apparent to the trained observer. Today we are merely continuing in the old way, remote as that path may be. Social stresses are a phenomenon in the lives of all created things from the amoeba to man himself, but we who belong to a superior class of creatures should use our powers of foresight, restraint, fair play, and a general charitable outlook on life if we hope to rise above the gross and disastrous results of a false sense of well-being merely because we are not willing to accept the truth of age-old experiences that followed precisely similar lines. We must not allow ourselves to return to the cave-man code of living because *that* code was merely an incident in the life of a creature of untaught and unguided proclivities.

We now recognize the extreme crudity and animal-like quality of such a mode of life, even though it was sufficient for its day and time. Virtually we know better, having been thoroughly taught by bitter experience and expedience, yet not listening to the wise and inspired advice of our inner conscience. What constitutes that inner conscience, where it resides in our mental store-house of knowledge, and how it managed to develop in the first place, are all questions of vital importance to our actual continuation of the human race upon this planet. It would be a matter for congratulation if the world of man would simply stop for a few years its mad rush towards a so-called *improved* existence. Perhaps during that period of materialistic somnolence we might have time to think, to cogitate, to look backward for guidance and suggestion, and not feel that we must everlastingly plunge ahead towards a totally unknown goal of very doubtful value. Mere onward progression is after all only one phase of living because the word "onward" has so little meaning in the last analysis. We cannot agree with the oft repeated statement that if we stand still we automatically go backward. Standing still to recover one's mental equilibrium is for a time a most useful and necessary part of life, especially after a headlong acceleration of every faculty has taxed our system almost to the point of exhaustion. The craze for novelty merely for its own sake is one of man's more childish qualities, and while it does have the advantage of keeping us momentarily interested, it in no way contributes anything of lasting value to our social structure, nor does it improve our mentality in a permanent way. More particularly, it savors always of the commercial aspect of our daily regime, a most distressing and altogether too important feature in the course of man's development.

Originally, as we learn from our study of early man, barter was one of the first signs of man's growing independence and grasp of world affairs, as he knew them when that world comprised comparatively little of the earth's surface. Such substances as amber, the fossilized gum of an ancient tree, pieces of which were found along the shores of the Baltic Sea, was a favorite article of trade among many European peoples during the Late Stone and Bronze periods of European prehistory. Sea shells, also gathered for the most part in Mediterranean waters, occur in many finds of prehistoric relics, often in places far removed from the ocean itself. Both amber and shells were evidently very attractive to early man and, we cannot doubt to his consort for use in making of ornaments for personal adornment. Necklaces, earrings, brooches, and other treasured pieces were popular among the tribal elite in many countries of the ancient world long before the use of money as a purchasing agent had ever occurred to our ancestors.

Today man does not barter with his neighbors in the old accepted sense of the word, but he does exchange his money for something which he wishes to possess. As the world population has vastly increased from year to year, especially in civilized countries, the merchant and the business of exchange which he represents have become such a power in our communal life that they bid fair to assume a role of overimportance in man's affairs. Aided by mechanical means such as the radio and cinema programs, the desirability of countless articles is presented in such a way as to catch the public attention and thus ensure a possible sale. To bolster immensely these sales and the consequent profits to the advertisers, the technologists in every division of man's activities are constantly being called upon to invent new objects, new techniques, and new substances in the hope of attracting buyers. There is nothing inherently wrong or vicious in these practices, but nevertheless after sober thought it will be realized that far too much attention is focused upon the daily wonders of technological achievement, interesting and valuable as it may be, and that an infantile habit to "see the birdie" is assiduously cultivated among the world's restless and credulous inhabitants. As long as man considers this state of mind the supreme goal of possible achievement, he will remain in his present status as a mere adolescent, unworthy of being a type of ani-

mal—unparalleled in all the history of creation—
who is capable of understanding the great truths of
life.

By the truth we mean the long series of splendid
discoveries in all branches of science which have
graced the pages of man's brilliant research record
during the centuries following his emergence from
barbarism. The inspiring story began somewhere
in our later prehistoric period when so many of
man's supreme characteristics began their approach
to perfection. Since that time a host of devoted men
in various parts of the world have brought to light
a series of extraordinary facts and principles relating
to many of nature's most fundamental secrets. Proof
of the presence of these all-pervading forces, with
their inevitable reactions under certain conditions, is
in itself a matter of epochal interest, while the long
continuing array of discoveries beneficial to humanity
in general is too numerous to mention. These seekers
for the truth, many of them martyred by their incredibly prejudiced contemporaries, are to be regarded with reverence and admiration by all thinking
men. Pure scientific research, pursued without thought
of monetary gain or other advantages, is surely one
of man's grandest concepts. When coupled with the
intense desire to unlock the door of the chamber of
knowledge, it is a proof of his close affinity with the
higher realms of spiritual understanding.

It is unfortunate, then, that under these circumstances humanity elects to waste both time and energy upon the pursuit of its false gods, living in a state of confusion about the comparative worth of the various factors which enter into the very fibers of our existence. A genuine understanding of the truth will not include an all-embracing interest in things material, but will seek to relegate to their proper position all factors entering into the life of a human being, placing high in the category an appreciation of those finer qualities with which man is so uniquely and so richly endowed. Only by a reverent and careful comparison of our primitive beginnings with our subsequent magnificent emergence from those long ages of intellectual darkness can we see man facing the perils and the rewards of the future with confidence and understanding.